More CHOICES

EAT WELL • LIVE WELL

P9-DNI-336

CHERYL D. THOMAS-PETERS, RD
James A. Peters, MD, DrPH, RD

30-minute Meals
Meal Planning • 12 Guidelines to Health

REVIEW AND HERALD® PUBLISHING ASSOCIATION
HAGERSTOWN, MD 21740

Editors . . . . .Jeannette R. Johnson and Patricia Fritz
Copy Editor . . . . .Jocelyn R. Fay
Cover Design . . . . .Patricia Wegh
Interior Design . . . . .Meyer Design
Art Director . . . . .Robin Meyer
Photographer . . . . .Paul Poplis
Photographer of Authors . . .Joseph's Photographic Design
Food Stylist . . . . .Carmen Himes
Assistant Food Stylist . . . .Kathy Walsh

The authors assume full responsibility for the accuracy of all facts and quotations as cited in this book.

R&H Cataloging Service

Peters, Cheryl Thomas, 1962-
Peters, James A., 1951-

    More Choices

    1. Vegetarian cookery.   I. Title.

        641.5636

ISBN 0-8280-1794-8

To order additional copies of this book, call **1-800-765-6955.**
Visit us at our website: **www.reviewandherald.com**

DEDICATION

I have dedicated each of my books to someone special in my life—to my mother, Carol Sims-Thomas, who patiently taught me the art of cooking and the joy of entertaining; to my daughter, Cherié, that she might share in my joy of food styling and preparation; to my son, Kent, because of his exceptional enjoyment of healthy foods and his ability to critique my recipes constructively.

This book is dedicated to my father, Kenneth D. Thomas, who inspired me to believe that I could achieve anything I put my heart into. He has encouraged me to write each of my cookbooks and to use my talents for God. My successes in life have been greater because of his constant motivation and inspiration. I love you, Daddy!

ACKNOWLEDGMENTS

Our gratitude to all those who contributed their talents to make this book a success . . . to our families and friends for contributing ideas and inspiring our books, and to our patients and seminar attendees, who have been our "living textbooks" and have taught us the direct benefits that can be achieved by making healthy choices.

Special thanks to Joseph's Photographic Design for the photographs of the authors.

Contents

Introduction

More Choices is a book for everyone who wants to eat well and be well. *More Choices* is an invitation to explore nutrition and lifestyle choices that will change your life and the way you look at food. *More Choices'* goal is to provide a better understanding of nutrition and lifestyle. It explores the relationships between diet and disease. More Choices is about enjoying the variety and abundance of good foods that lead to better health.

More Choices begins with 12 Guidelines for Health, which identifies what the ideal lifestyle is to promote health and prevent disease. The 12 Guidelines for Health were built on the latest scientific research on nutrition and health and Scripture's counsel on diet and health.

Our Meal Planning Guide summarizes these proven guidelines for better health from science and Scripture and makes them practical. You'll see how to package these health-promoting foods into great-tasting, easy-to-prepare family meals. It involves simple changes that you can make over time. It is an eating strategy aimed at improving your health instead of a diet aimed solely at helping you shed pounds, or lower cholesterol, or regulate bloods sugar. Such questions as "How do I stop sugar-cravings and snacking?"; "Are carbohydrates fattening?"; and "Is a high-protein diet best for weight loss?" are answered.

In our *More Choices* Meal Planning Guide there are no foods to weigh; no adding up fat grams; no complicated food exchange lists to follow; no odd food combining. Our guide features a Plant-based Food Pyramid designed to simplify meal planning. Foods that have been proved to improve health and reduce risk of disease were chosen. Cooking techniques and food storage tips are given to help nutrient-rich foods preserve their health-promoting ingredients when they reach the table.

More Choices features more than 120 taste-tested family-favorite recipes that are delicious, easy to prepare, health-promoting, and can be made in 30 minutes or less. Our meals are built on plant-based foods with or without the addition of low-fat dairy products and eggs. These uncomplicated recipes help you understand what a healthy diet means and how to put it into action.

More Choices is for those who eat meat, are trying to eat less meat, are trying to eat more plant-based foods, or are following a completely plant-based diet. More Choices promises a successful transition to increasing the intact plant-based foods in your diet and decreasing refined foods such as white bread, white flour, white refined sugar, and animal foods.

More Choices promises to answer the questions about how we live better, feel better, and live longer. The 12 Guidelines for Health and the Meal Planning Guide suggest lifestyle changes, and the 120 family-favorite recipes promise to be easier and tastier, making this lifestyle plan something that you can stick with for a lifetime.

LIFESTYLE GUIDELINES TO BETTER HEALTH

Your lifestyle choices determine the quality and length of your life. **How you choose to live on a daily basis, all your actions and habits, is your lifestyle. Making the right choices enables you to experience health throughout your lifetime.**

"Health is a priceless treasure, valued most when lost. . . . Fame, education, position, money, are dearly purchased at the sacrifice of health" (The Home Physician and Guide to Health 1923 [1923], p. 75).

Poor health and disease do not come randomly. Each disease has a cause, in fact, most diseases have a number of factors that together contribute to a given disease. Factors found to increase your chances of getting sick are called risk factors.

Disease never comes without a cause. The way is prepared, and disease invited, by disregard of the laws of health" (The Ministry of Healing, p. 234).

Risk factors contribute to your chance of developing disease. Risk factors that are "fixed" (not changeable) are age, race, gender, heredity. Risk factors that are changeable are factors that you can do something about, because they are based on the way you live. These are referred to as "lifestyle" factors.

LIFESTYLE MEDICINE

Modifying how you live, your habits, your lifestyle, in order to get or stay healthy is the essence of preventive medicine, often referred to as lifestyle medicine. In these times of high medical costs and the epidemic of death from preventable diseases, it becomes critical to take control of your life.

Improving a lifestyle factor can decrease the severity of, slow the progression, and in some cases can even reverse the disease process. Much of the premature mortality—dying younger than we should—can be reduced by almost half through simple changes in how we live. The United States Centers for Disease Control and Prevention

estimates that if just one lifestyle risk factor was reduced for each of the chronic diseases, there would be a 47 percent reduction in mortality per year.

CHANGE YOUR HABITS . . . CHANGE YOUR LIFE

One third or more of the world's population suffers from the effects of poor health choices.

You or someone you know right now is most likely experiencing the effects of chronic illness. **Each year in the United States alone, more than 2 million people die from all causes.** The tragedy is that almost a million of these people die prematurely from conditions that are largely preventable. Seventy-five percent of these deaths are owing to chronic diseases such as heart disease, stroke, cancer, obstructive lung disease, diabetes, and chronic liver disease.

You have the power to choose the lifestyle that will either promote better health or promote disease! **This book will show you the health-promoting lifestyle factors and the steps to making the changes in your lifestyle practical for everyday living!** Our goal is to guide you to a plan of action – for a lifetime!

"Beloved, I pray that you may prosper in all things and be in health…" 3 John 2 New King James Bible

LIFESTYLE FACTORS INCREASING RISK OF ILLNESS OR DISEASE

- Smoking
- Being overweight
- Inactivity
- Diet
- Stress
- Lack of sleep
- Alcohol or use of other drugs
- Not drinking enough water
- Poor hygiene
- Lifestyle Medicine

WHAT IS HEALTH?

"Health is a state of energetic physical, mental, social, and spiritual well-being, and not simply the absence of disease. It is a balance of all areas of our life which results in our being energetic, feeling alive, feeling comfortable, and being at peace with ourselves, others, and God"

James A. Peters, MD, DrPH, RD

Medical Definition of Health:

The medical definition of health is scientific, but we believe there is more to good health. The medical concept of health is based on what is normal or average. Blood pressure, cholesterol, weight, and other measures are considered normal when they are within the average ranges for people who are free of known disease. If your doctor can find no illness upon exam, and all of your measured values are within normal limits, you are considered healthy.

We believe there is more to health than just the lack of disease! When God created human beings, the first thing He did was tell us how to live to achieve optimal health. As we compare science and Scripture regarding nutrition and lifestyle for optimal health, we find similar lifestyle factors recommended for promoting health and preventing disease.

The following is God's definition of health as identified at Creation!

FOUR PARTS OF HEALTH LEADING TO WHOLENESS:

1. Mental Function

Dominion over—identifies the **mental**, cognitive, and management function of humanity. *"Then God said, 'Let Us make man in Our image, according to Our likeness; let them have dominion over'"* all other living things
(Genesis 1:26, NKJV).

The mind controls the body. It is with your mind that you relate to others and God. Through your mind you become knowledgeable about God's laws of health, and make choices that promote your body's health. The health of the body determines the health of the mind.

"A contented mind, a cheerful spirit, is health to the body and strength to the soul"
(The Ministry of Healing, p. 241).

Good nutrition, fresh air, avoidance of sedating or mind-altering drugs is crucial to optimize the brains function and let us hear God's *"still small voice"*
(1 Kings 19:12).

"The consciousness of rightdoing is one of the best medicines for diseased bodies and minds"
(The Ministry of Healing, p. 257).

"A merry heart does good, like medicine"
(Proverbs 17:22, NKJV).

2. Social

God created us to be social beings. Positive relationships with others promote health and well-being. Pursuing the friendship of others is God-ordained. This is an important part of health. Poor relationships lead to distrust, depression, anxiety, loss of productivity, worry, and stress. Studies show that if you are in a supportive, positive, honest relationship, your health and longevity improve.

THE PRINCIPLES OF SOCIAL RELATIONSHIPS BEGIN WITH THE FAMILY UNIT.

"He created . . . male and female"
(Genesis 1:27, NKJV).
"It is not good that man should be alone; I will make him a helper comparable to him"
(Genesis 2:18, NKJV).

"Husbands, love your wives, just as Christ also loved the church, and gave Himself for her"
(Ephesians 5:25, NKJV).

HEALTHY RELATIONSHIPS IMPROVE YOUR PHYSICAL AND MENTAL WELL-BEING AND INCREASE YOUR HEALTH AND LENGTH OF LIFE.

3. Physical

The health of the physical body determines the health of the mind. It is through the mind that all the other relationships are developed—social and spiritual. Keeping the physical body healthy was so important that one of the first things God did when He created man and woman was to prescribe a diet. God prescribed a plant-based diet for us. God prescribed a diet to care for the **physical** part of health.

"And God said, 'See, I have given you every herb that yields seed which is on the face of all the earth, and every tree whose fruit yields seed; to you it shall be for food'"

(Genesis 1:29, NKJV).

More Choices **focuses on the nutritional component of being healthy!**

4. Spiritual

The spiritual part of humans is the key relationship that needs to be in place for true health. It is so important that God set aside a whole day to nourish this component. Prayer, meditation, and communion with God have strong health benefits. Connecting with God infuses healing into all of our relationships. Just like the sun is the energy source for our solar system, so the Son of God is our energy (life) source.

"And on the seventh day God ended His work which He had done, and He rested on the seventh day. . . . Then God blessed the seventh day and sanctified it"

(Genesis 2:2,3, NKJV).

When you distrust God, the spiritual relationship is broken, causing disruption in all other relationships of your life. To become whole again, all of the components of health must be brought back into balance. Since you have been created in the image of God, you must be reconciled to God through faith (trust) in what He has done and is doing for you. God's plan of salvation is the good news, for this is the plan of restoration—restoration to wholeness and true, complete health.

"In Him was life and the life was the light of men. . . . That was the true Light which gives light to every man coming into the world" (John 1:4-9, NKJV). "I am the light of the world" (John 9:5, NKJV).

"And the very God of peace sanctify you wholly: and I pray God your whole spirit and soul and body be preserved blameless" (1 Thessalonians 5:23). God makes you whole. He restores and saves **all** *of you.*

WHOLENESS COMES WHEN THE FOUR PARTS OF HEALTH ARE MET!

The Bible's concept of being healthy is to be whole. To be whole (true health) is to have a balanced relationship in each of these 4 key components to health.

The Hebrew and Greek words for health in the Bible carry the meanings "to be whole," or "saved." The Bible draws no distinction between being healthy and being saved, therefore, how we become a better Christian is also how we become more healthy.

"True religion not only emphasizes the accountability of man to God for the preservation and care of his body, but it also restores to him the governing power over his appetite" (The Home Physician and Guide to Health [1923], p. 75).

12 GUIDELINES TO BETTER HEALTH

These 12 guidelines focus on the practical application of science and scripture and their recommendations for better health. These simple, natural remedies are proven to promote health and prevent disease.

12 GUIDLINES TO BETTER HEALTH

1. Enjoy fresh air.
2. Drink a minimum of eight glasses of water daily.
3. Eat wholesome, unrefined, plant-based foods.
4. Exercise daily—30 to 60 minutes.
5. Get adequate sleep and rest—seven to nine hours daily.
6. Get modest sunshine—minimum of 30 minutes per day.
7. Avoid alcohol and other drugs.
8. Observe the rules of cleanliness and good hygiene.
9. Maintain a positive attitude.
10. Cherish good relationships.
11. Wear appropriate clothing for temperature, circulation, and movement.
12. Trust in God's power.

1. Enjoy Fresh Air.

Any activity that limits the fresh air you breathe, will affect your well-being. Avoid smoking; unnecessary exposure to air pollutants; poor posture; shallow, improper breathing; tight, restrictive clothing, etc.

Smoking is the single greatest preventable cause of death in the United States—430,000 deaths per year. There is no other single activity that compromises our health as much as breathing smoke on a regular basis.

AIR (OXYGEN) IS A PART OF NUTRITION

"In order to have good blood, we must breathe well. Full, deep inspirations of pure air, which fill the lungs with oxygen, purify the blood. They impart to it a bright color and send it, a life-giving current, to every part of the body. A good respiration soothes the nerves; it stimulates the appetite and renders digestion more perfect; and it induces sound, refreshing sleep."

—The Ministry of Healing, p. 272

Air is needed to release the energy from the food you have eaten. This release of energy from food is called "metabolism," and this process creates heat. Oxygen has to be present for your metabolic fires to burn. Without the air you breathe, your metabolic fires will go out and you will die. Air (oxygen) is a part of nutrition, since food cannot be metabolized without it.

WATER

- Makes up to 60 to 70 percent of our body
- Provides the medium for the body's chemical reactions
- Allows for elimination of waste
- Regulates body temperature
- Cleans the body when applied externally
- Improves endurance
- Lowers heart disease risk

2. Drink Fresh Water—Six to Eight Glasses Daily.

Drink fluids frequently throughout the day, preferably before feeling thirsty. It is recommended to drink six to eight glasses of water daily. More is needed if temperatures are high or heavy work is performed.

Sufficient water intake with exercise has been proven to increase endurance by 20 to 30 percent. Recent studies find that adequate water intake lowers heart disease risk.

3. Eat Wholesome, Unrefined, Plant-based Foods.

Food is as vital to your body as air and water. The body's primary concern is for energy (calories) so that your organs can function, and you have energy to do the things you choose. This energy is obtained from the food you eat.

Plants are our body's best source of energy. They capture the sun's energy and put that energy into three packages usable for people and animals: carbohydrate, protein, and fat.

Research studies have repeatedly shown that plant-based foods provide for the best endurance and the lowest risk for cancers, heart disease, and diabetes, and help in maintaining a proper weight.

Build your meals on unrefined, whole foods, such as whole grains, beans, legumes, whole vegetables and fruits, nuts and seeds. These unrefined foods are loaded with the optimal energy for health promotion and endurance,. Plant-foods are also loaded with vitamins, minerals, and disease protective phytochemicals. They are cholesterol-free, low in fat (except for nuts and avocados—which contain "essential" fat), and contain adequate levels of protein for growth and tissue repair, and adequate carbohydrates for endurance. Eat a variety of plant-based foods of all types and colors in sufficient quantities to assure good health and to maintain your ideal weight.

Are animal foods necessary for good health?

We believe, and hundreds of scientific research studies confirm, that obtaining packaged energy directly from the plants is healthier than getting it secondhand, after it has been processed by the animals who first ate the plants.

"Returning to a predominantly plant-based diet may be the single most important thing we can do, as a group, for our health."

—B. Stavric, PhD, Patient Care, Nov. 15, 1995, p. 36.

ANIMAL FOODS ARE REFINED FOODS.

Animals eat the plant food first. Their digestion and metabolism process refines the food—losing fiber, carbohydrates, phytochemicals, and other nutrient-rich ingredients. Other substances are added by the animal that can be harmful—saturated fat, cholesterol, animal hormones, viral and bacterial organisms that the animal might be harboring! When meat is eaten it is then a refined food!

Meat, poultry, and fish are clearly refined foods!

Many believe that we are free to eat anything we want, and that is true!

"All things are lawful for me, but not all things are helpful"

(I Corinthians 10:23, NKJV).

Currently there is an increase in animal disease; worry about the spread of "mad cow" disease; widespread use of antibiotics in animals with residuals left over in the meat that is consumed—and development of resistant strains of bacteria; superficial and inadequate meat inspections; the "refined" quality of meat; and the undesirable saturated fat, cholesterol, and other substances in meat. We cannot see any benefits from consuming animal products.

Because our body's is the "temple of God," 1 Corinthians 6:19, it becomes a moral issue to strive for the healthiest body we can have.

The first temptation of man and woman involved food. Making good food choices is still difficult for most people. You may be tempted to eat foods that are not always the best for you. Knowing this, and accepting this fact, you truly need to let God lead you and give you strength to make healthy food choices. See step 12, Trust in God's power. Our goal is to be as healthy as we can be in all areas of our life.

"Therefore, whether you eat or drink, or whatever you do, do all to the glory of God" (1 Corinthians 10:31, NKJV).

We recommend and personally follow God's original plant-based diet because we feel that this is the diet originally given to humanity and because current scientific research reconfirms that God's prescription for good health—a plant-based diet—is the best!

The prophet Daniel also believed and followed God's original diet.

PROPHET DANIEL'S NUTRITIONAL EXPERIMENT

The prophet Daniel, in the Old Testament, conducted the first nutritional experiment because he believed that God would bless him with good health if he followed God's original diet.

"Daniel purposed in his heart that he would not defile himself with the portion of the king's delicacies. . . . And at the end of ten days their features appeared better and fatter in flesh than all the young men who ate the portion of the king's delicacies" (Daniel 1:8-15, NKJV).

Daniel and his friends were blessed in health and wisdom. "And in all matters of wisdom and understanding about which the king examined them, he found them **ten times better**" (verse 20, NKJV).
Do you want to be 10 times wiser and healthier?
God blessed Daniel and his friends for making healthier choices, and He promises to do the same for us. Would you like your kids to be 10 times wiser and healthier? We've got the answer. Follow God's original plan for your diet, as did Daniel!

Science confirms in hundreds of studies what Scripture recommends. Eating plant-based foods— grains, beans, vegetables, fruits, nuts, and seeds—can promote health and prevent disease!

4. Exercise Daily—30 to 60 Minutes.

"Action is a law of our being."

—The Ministry of Healing, p. 237.

THE FOLLOWING SHOULD BE IMPLEMENTED DAILY FOR 30 TO 60 MINUTES

Stretching—stretching and moving all joints to their maximum range of motion. This will keep our muscles and tendons flexible and strong.

Resistance—Resistant-type exercises stimulate the muscles and nerves of the body. Light weights, exercise stretch bands, or some types of work provide this type of exercise.

Aerobic—Aerobic exercises such as walking are excellent exercises that engage large muscles of the body and can keep a person fit. **Outdoor exercise is preferable to indoor, providing fresh air, sunlight, and activity.**

It is important to move all the major muscles and joints in your body daily. Our goal is to stimulate the body through activity by increasing the heart rate and breathing rate. Start slow and gradually work toward higher intensity as is safe for your current physical condition.

Exercise helps to strengthen muscle and improve circulation. Bones get stronger, and bone thinning (osteoporosis) is inhibited. Blood sugar is regulated better; good cholesterol (HDL) is increased; body weight and excess fat stores are controlled; heart, lung, gastrointestinal, and mental function all improve.

EXERCISE IS AN EXCELLENT ANTIDEPRESSANT.

The consensus from the Adventist Health Study and the Harvard University Alumni Studies found that exercise can extend your life by two more years. (*New England Journal of Medicine,* 314 [1986]: 605-613).

A 70-year-old person, physically active, can achieve fitness equivalent to that of a sedentary 30-year-old.

—*Journal of American Medical Association,* 261 (1989); 3590-3598.

Doctor's Warning: If you decide to <u>stay</u> sedentary, be sure to get your doctor's permission. Prolonged inactivity is dangerous to your health.

5. Get Adequate Sleep and Rest.

Rest and sleep are as important as exercise. Good health requires activity should be followed by periods of rest. There must be a balance. It is during the periods of rest that muscle development actually occurs. But without the exercise, there would be no muscle development during the rest period. It is during sleep that the body rejuvenates itself.

Sleeping seven to nine hours per night for adults is optimal, with more or less than this amount of sleep being associated with greater morbidity and mortality.

Sleep allows for repair of body tissues and rejuvenates the immune system. Sleep has also been found to improve learning and memory.

Antiaging effect of Adequate Sleep.

During the sleep hours, growth hormone is released from the pituitary. Growth hormone has been called the "antiaging" hormone of the body. Miss your sleep and you miss important releases of this vital hormone.

6. Get Modest Sunlight—
Minimum of 30 Minutes per Day.

SUNSHINE

- Source of energy, photosynthesis packages this energy in plants.
- Elevates mood.
- Makes vitamin D
- Kills germs, both bacteria and viruses.
- Synchronizes body functions.
- Influences body hormones.

Sunlight is not as commonly talked about except when warning about overexposure to prevent skin cancers. Sunlight is essential for good health.

- **Sunlight is the source of energy** that plants capture by way of photosynthesis and package into the food we eat—carbohydrates, protein, fat.
- **A 15- to 30-minute exposure to sunlight** can provide you with the recommended daily quota of vitamin D. Vitamin D is synthesized from the cholesterol under the skin when sunlight acts on it.
- **Light improves one's mood.** For some people, depression can result when there are insufficient daylight hours such as during the winter months. This has been termed seasonal affective disorder (SAD), and it can indeed make them sad! Exercising outdoors is also recognized as an effective natural antidepressant, the exercise itself contributing to this beneficial effect.
- **Allowing sunlight to shine into your home** helps not only to elevate your mood, but also to sanitize your home. Sunlight is an important disinfectant and is able to kill both bacteria and viruses. In a room, bacteria levels are lowest near an outside window.
- **Light also helps synchronize your body's biological clock** so that you function and feel better.
- **Light affects your body's hormones.** The primary hormone affected is melatonin. Melatonin is important for helping you sleep, and it also has an effect on sex hormones. Melatonin slows down some sex hormone production. Too much light can increase sex hormone production. We see this with the invention of electricity. At the turn of the twentieth-century, menstruation started at an average age of 16 to 17 years. Now average age of menstruation is 11 to 12 years of age. Many attribute this to the invention of artificial light and possibly a high-protein intake. We find that earlier menstruation accelerates the aging process. Chicken ranchers use this to their advantage by using 24-hour-per-day light to get an increase in egg production. But the result is that chickens burn out in two to three years and stop producing eggs.

"The pure air, the glad sunshine, the flower and trees, the orchards and vineyards, and outdoor exercise amid these surroundings, are health-giving, life-giving"

(The Ministry of Healing, p. 264).

"Whoever sleeps in a sunless room, or occupies a bed that has not been thoroughly dried and aired, does so at the risk of health"

(The Ministry of Healing, p. 275).

7. Avoid Alcohol and Other Drugs.

Many use alcohol and drugs as an escape from physical or emotional pain in their life. The use of these harmful substances becomes the only way that people see to cope with stresses of life. Initially alcohol will make you feel good—but no problems are solved.

Some find that just one drink can uninhibit them just enough to be more social at a party. That seems innocent enough to most. Others have no stopping point and cannot control their addictions and become what society defines as truly addicted. This is the point where all the relationships in the person's life begin to fall apart, jobs are lost, and the person cannot function in society's definition as normal.

The truth is that any intake of alcohol and drugs, small or large amounts, is harmful. It is wise to avoid substances that alter the function of the brain and nervous system. Your brain is the distinguishing organ that separates you from other animals. Alcohol diminishes the brains ability to discriminate between subtle choices and between right and wrong.

Drugs and alcohol are the major culprits of health-destroying addictions. Destroyed health, loss of money, loss of relationships, destroyed families, and crime are reasons enough to avoid these substances. The small benefit that wine may give to decreasing heart disease is far outweighed by its adverse effects. In fact, the same health protective benefits found in wine are from the grape, and fresh grapes or juice provide the benefits without the sedation or risk of addiction. It has been shown that with positive changes in lifestyle and diet, wine is not necessary for the prevention of heart disease.

Alcohol is a sedative. It is a toxin to all of our cells and is especially deleterious to our liver and nerve cells. It cannot be recommended. There are more than 100,000 deaths each year in the United States directly attributable to alcohol use. Alcohol is one of the primary causes of liver disease, making mortality because of liver failure one of the leading causes of death in the United States.

"Wine is a mocker, strong drink is raging: and whosoever is deceived thereby is not wise" (Proverbs 20:1). "Look not thou upon the wine when it is red, when it giveth its colour in the cup, when it moveth itself aright. At the last it biteth like a serpent, and stingeth like an adder"

(Proverbs 23:31, 32).

Like the recommendation for women who are pregnant—there is no safe levels of alcohol—we believe that this recommendation should apply to everyone. The essence of addictions is that we continue to engage in a habit, behavior, or use of a substance, despite its having unhealthy outcomes. With regular use, it becomes most difficult to stop without heroic efforts, special programs, or Higher Power intervention.

We believe that when any of the four parts of health (mental, social, physical, spiritual—as listed in a previous section) are not in balance in our lives, we lose our ability to cope with stress. Life is full of stress, and we need to find balance in our lives—true wholeness. Without wholeness, we begin looking for a quick fix! Alcohol, painkillers, illegal drugs, etc., all give that quick fix—with a big price to pay in the future. The real pain and stress do not go away until God can bring wholeness into our lives.

8. Observe the Rules of Cleanliness and Good Hygiene.

Generous amounts of fresh drinking water cleanse the inside of the body and allow for the chemistry of life to occur. Likewise, cleaning the outside of our bodies by frequent bathing helps preserve our health. Washing one's hands is a first defense against the spread of disease. Keeping food and food preparation areas clean goes a long way in stopping the epidemic of food poisoning.

"Scrupulous cleanliness is essential to both physical and mental health. Impurities are constantly thrown off from the body through the skin. Its millions of pores are quickly clogged unless kept clean by frequent bathing" (The Ministry of Healing, p. 276).

9. Maintain a Positive Attitude.

You must cultivate an attitude that is positive. "Whatsoever things are true, . . . honest, . . . just, . . . pure, . . . lovely, . . . of good report; if there be any virtue, and if there be any praise, think on these things" (Philippians 4:8). Use the gift of self-control to help you choose those things that are positive to think about. This improves your mental, social, and physical well-being.

"A merry heart doeth good like a medicine."
—Proverbs 17:22.

"The relation that exists between the mind and the body is very intimate. . . . Many of the diseases from which men suffer are the result of mental depression. Grief, anxiety, discontent, remorse, guilt, distrust, all tend to break down the life forces and to invite decay and death. . . . Courage, hope, faith, sympathy, love, promote health and prolong life."
—The Ministry of Healing, p. 241.

10. Cherish Good Relationships With Family and Friends.

Receiving and giving love and care to other people gives your life meaning, enjoyment, purpose, and creates a sense of value. The act of giving of yourself to others has consistently shown to enhance one's health and well-being. Isaiah 58 promises that when you give to those in need, *"your healing shall spring forth speedily"* (verse 8, NKJV).

"Human love should draw its closest bonds from divine love. Only where Christ reigns can there be deep, true, unselfish affection" (The Ministry of Healing, p. 358).

It is in the context of an intimate relationship that God allows us to be a part of creating a new life. This brings together the family unit. It is within the family unit that we learn the real practical aspect of receiving and giving love.

11. Wear Appropriate Clothing for Temperature, Circulation, and Movement.

Good health requires good circulation. Dressing appropriately for the weather and work conditions is important. Clothing that is too tight or that does not provide for sufficient warmth when cold limits blood flow and compromises health. Clothes should be loose enough to allow for breathing freely and freedom of movement. Clothes should also help protect us from adverse elements, thereby protecting our skin from excess sunlight and other injuries to the skin.

"Instead of struggling to meet the demands of fashion, have the courage to dress healthfully and simply" (The Ministry of Healing, p. 294).

12. Trust in God's Power.

To be healthy requires that we trust in God and keep His health laws. *"Trust in the Lord, and do good"* (Psalm 37:3).

Many get discouraged in the process of trying to eat or live better. Many feel that it is too difficult to follow all of the health laws and change our habits. Statistics reveal relapse rates for weight loss average 70 to 80 percent and long-term weight loss success averages only 5 to 10 percent.

Keeping God's laws is really not difficult if we do it His way: *"The word is very near you, in your mouth and in your heart, that you may do it"* (Deuteronomy 30:14, NKJV). Note in John 1:1 that **the Word is Christ!** So with Christ in our hearts, we can keep God's law! This refers not only to the spiritual laws, but to the physical laws. God is creator of both.

The loss of health resulted when Adam and Eve distrusted God and ate what God had forbidden. Good health begins when we start trusting God and put Him back into our lives. This begins the healing process. The beginning of poor health was a result of distrust, not the forbidden food that was eaten.

Understanding and complying with the laws of health assure optimal health. The violation of any of God's laws weakens our system and invites disease. Recognize that transgression of the law produces affliction (see Psalm 107:17).

However, if we obey His commandments (spiritual and physical laws), we can enter into life (see Matthew 19:17).

The good news is that God has given you the tools to become healthy and make the right choices—to do the things we should do rather than the things we want to do. When you trust God, He gives us these gifts: *"love, joy, peace, patience, kindness, goodness, faithfulness, gentleness and self-control"* **(Galatians 5:22, 23, NIV).**

SELF-CONTROL IS A GIFT FROM GOD.

Self-control is the tool you use to become healthy— doing those things you should and avoiding those things that are harmful—it is a gift from God. When you trust God and accept His gifts to you, He <u>gives</u> you the POWER to change (John 1:12). **God provides the power to enable us to develop the good habits that promote and restore health.**

"I can do all things through Christ who strengthens me" **(Philippians 4:13, NKJV).** This is where you get the strength to follow through on your healthy choices—to eat better, to exercise more, to make lifestyle choices.

To be accepted, to live without guilt, are powerful physical, mental, and social medicines. In fact, the key to antiaging is what only God can give us—" *that whoever believes in Him shall not perish but have eternal life"* (John 3:16, NKJV).

To be able to live forever—that is ultimate health. **When these concepts are grasped, the struggle of trying to achieve health through our own efforts is over.**

"For by grace you have been saved [made whole] through faith, and that not of yourselves; it is the gift of God, not of works, lest anyone should boast" **(Ephesians 2:8, 9, NKJV).**

"Thy faith hath made thee whole"

(Matthew 9:22).

The path to becoming healthy
is then through faith—

just like it is for salvation by faith.

We call this *"health by faith."*

SCIENCE CONFIRMS THAT APPLYING THESE 12 LIFESTYLE GUIDELINES WILL PROMOTE HEALTH AND PREVENT DISEASE.

Does lifestyle really matter? The Health Habit study conducted over a period of 12 years by Drs. Nedra Belloc and Lester Breslow demonstrated some important, powerful findings. They followed 6,928 people and how well they followed seven simple health habits:

- No smoking
- Little or no alcohol
- Daily exercise
- Breakfast daily
- No snacking
- Normal weight
- Seven to nine hours sleep per night

The results showed an amazing life expectancy gain of 11.5 years in those people who practiced six to seven of these health habits regularly compared with those who reported practicing less than three of these habits!

These are simple lifestyle habits with profound lifetime effects on our health. We incorporated these lifestyle habits into our 12 Guidelines for Health.

Practicing simple health habits can increase your lifespan by 11.5 years!

Adventists were used in many health studies because they are a large group of people who follow a predominantly plant-based diet without the addition of alcohol, drugs, and smoking.

The Adventist Health Study followed 34,000 Seventh-day Adventists for more than 11 years. They found significant advantages to healthier living.

- A plant-based diet increased life span by five years in men and four years in women.

◆ ◆ ◆ ◆ ◆ ◆ ◆ ◆ ◆ ◆ ◆ ◆ ◆ ◆ ◆ ◆ ◆ ◆ ◆ ◆

- The eating of predominantly unrefined foods in the diet gave a three-year life span advantage.
- Exercise provided a 2 year lifetime advantage.

These studies looked at longevity; however, in the process of extending life through nutrition and lifestyle changes, we find that the quality and daily function of your life improve. This makes all the changes worth it!

FOLLOWING A PLANT-BASED DIET CAN ADD FOUR TO FIVE YEARS TO YOUR LIFE —AND ADDS LIFE TO YOUR YEARS!

Modest changes in diet and lifestyle have also shown to help prevent diabetes, which has reached epidemic proportions in the United States. Middle-aged men and women who were overweight and had impaired blood glucose levels (prediabetic) were instructed to change the following lifestyle factors:

- Lose weight
- Decrease total fat intake
- Decrease saturated fat intake
- Increase dietary fiber intake
- Increase exercise

Conclusion: Over a three-year period there was a 58 percent decrease in risk of developing diabetes compared to those who did not make these changes.

Type 2 Diabetes can be prevented by changes in lifestyles.
—New England Journal of Medicine, May 2001

Numerous research studies document that simple changes in diet and lifestyle reduce the risk of heart disease, cancer, stroke, diabetes, liver disease, and emphysema and chronic bronchitis. Consistently it is shown that you "get back what you put in." The more healthy changes you make, the greater the health benefits you experience.

Diabetes and coronary heart disease have also been shown to be reversible in some people who were motivated and committed to making significant nutrition and lifestyle changes in their life.

When you start to apply these lifestyle and nutrition guidelines, as outlined in this book, it may seem as if you cannot see any immediate improvement. Over time; however, there will be **measurable changes in your body.**

MEASURABLE SIGNS OF IMPROVEMENT FROM FOLLOWING THESE 12 LIFESTYLE GUIDLINES

- Less heartburn and indigestion
- Lower blood pressure
- Lower cholesterol and triglycerides
- Weight moving closer to your ideal
- Less constipation
- Better blood sugar regulation
- Less need for medications used for chronic problems
- Improved sleep at night
- Less depression
- More energy
- A sense of well-being

Health is a process, not a destination. Daily, we must make the right choices. Just like swimming or riding a bicycle, you must keep moving to stay on top. An athlete who is in good shape can lose his fitness edge in as little as one to two weeks of inactivity. Athletic performance requires regular daily exercise to stay in shape. To be healthy you must live healthy, make healthy choices, and take action on these choices on a daily basis. Being healthy is not a one-time event, but a lifetime process.

Consistent application of simple principles with God's leading is the way to achieve health and wholeness. Eating breakfast daily, drinking more water, increasing fruit and vegetables in the diet, eating more plant-based unrefined foods, exercise—all are simple principles that promote health and prevent disease!

Remember, being healthy is a PROCESS. It is not something you achieve and you're done. Making the best lifestyle choices on a daily basis makes you as healthy as you can ever be for that day—and that is all that is required to be successful!

DAILY APPLICATION OF SIMPLE PRINCIPLES LEADS TO BETTER HEALTH.

PRINCIPLES FOR BUILDING HEALTHY MEALS

1. Center your meals on a wide variety of plant foods.

Plant foods should be the foundation of your meals. For maximum benefit, include a wide variety of grains, legumes, vegetables, and fruits, in addition to small amounts of nuts and seeds.

Plant foods provide abundant nutrients, fiber, and phytochemicals without the cholesterol and saturated fat found in animal foods. The plant-based food pyramid will guide you in planning great-tasting meals that promote health for you and your family. Be sure to obtain adequate quantities of these foods.

2. Eat two cups or two pieces of fresh fruit or vegetables at every meal!

Include at least one cup of berries per day.

"Lack of fruits and vegetables is the greatest nutrition deficiency in our country."

Fruits and vegetables are loaded with essential vitamins, minerals, phytochemicals, and soluble and insoluble fibers. Eat a variety of different types and colors of fruits and vegetables. Different colors contain different nutrients. So variety of color will provide the broad spectrum of nutrients we need.

Berries are nutrient-rich powerhouses known for their disease-preventive qualities.

We recommend one cup per day of fresh (or frozen unsweetened) whole berries daily!

They contain phytochemicals that fight against some cancers. Research has shown them to improve brain speed. They contain powerful antioxidant properties. It is not just one nutrient in the berry that is giving this health-promoting effect; therefore, research shows that supplementation of individual nutrients does not give the same disease-preventive qualities.

Remember, many of these essential vitamins are water-soluble and need to be eaten two to three times per day and many are absorbed best with meals. Research shows that when these essential vitamins and minerals are eaten in whole foods instead of from supplements we see a

much better result. The whole foods contain other phytochemicals and fiber not found in the supplements and appear to be better utilized by the body.

3. Eat whole foods versus refined foods. Choose foods in their natural state!

Whole grains, fresh fruits, and vegetables are loaded with fiber, and many valuable vitamins, minerals, and phytochemicals can be lost in the refining process. Both soluble and insoluble fiber are protective against disease. Eat whole foods!

If a first grader cannot read all the ingredients on the food label, don't eat it. **Favor foods that need no food label, like fresh fruits and vegetables.**

4. Limit your fat intake, especially trans-fatty acids and saturated fats. Avoid oxidized fat.

Favor monounsaturated fats such as olives, nuts, seeds, and avocados from the fat group. These foods provide the essential fatty acids and promote health when eaten in moderation. Limit all fats, particularly hydrogenated or trans-fatty acids and saturated fats. Trans-fats are found in margarine, vegetable shortening, and many processed foods with hydrogenated or partially hydrogenated oils. Saturated fats are found in animal foods and tropical oils.

Avoid oxidized or rancid fats; they are especially damaging to the body. Oxidized fats are from fats that are fried or have been open to the air and sunlight for extended periods of time.

Even those on a plant-based diet can get too much fat, especially if full-fat dairy products, eggs, fried foods, and sweet baked goods such as pies and cakes are eaten regularly.

5. Include a daily source of omega-3 fatty acids in your meals.

Omega-3 fatty acids are important in helping to maintain your health and preventing disease. Plant-food sources of omega-3 fatty acids include flax seeds, flax oils, canola oil, soy products, walnuts, leafy green vegetables, and wheat germ. Be sure to keep these foods in the refrigerator or freezer to prevent the fat from getting rancid.

6. Eat to achieve and maintain a healthy body weight.

Many diseases can be prevented by achieving your healthy body weight. The body mass index (BMI) is one method used for evaluating your optimal weight to give you the least risk for developing weight-related diseases. The BMI is calculated by dividing your weight in kilograms (kg.) by your height in meters squared (m.)^2.

BMI= eight (kg.)/height (m.)^2. Or you can check your body mass index (BMI) on our chart on page 141. The safest way to maintain a healthy body weight is to eat a varied, balanced diet and to exercise regularly.

7. Limit the use of refined sugars and salty foods.

Sugar is a source of high calories and is nutrient-poor. High sugar in the meals can also lead to tooth decay. The best sweets come packaged in nature as fruits. Use fruits for satisfying your sweet tooth!

Excess salty foods can contribute to hypertension or fluid retention, and can deplete calcium. Watch for salt in salty snack foods such as chips and crackers, and many prepared foods, pickled foods, and condiments.

8. Limit your use of smoked, charred, and cured foods.

These methods of preparing foods can increase exposure to carcinogens and should be minimized.

9. Use plant foods grown without the use of pesticides whenever possible.

Pesticide residues on foods can contribute to cancer and can be particularly harmful to children. Try to select foods grown without pesticides or with minimal use of pesticides. **Wash your fruits and vegetables with clean, fresh running water just before eating.** Do not soak your fruits and vegetables to clean them. Many times this allows the pesticide to simply soak into the skin through the stem areas of the fruits or vegetables and can actually increase our intake of pesticides.

10. Include a daily source of vitamin B12 and vitamin D.

A plant source of vitamin B12 is in nutritional yeast flakes or a daily supplement of two micrograms per day (3 micrograms needed in pregnancy and lactation). For those using dairy products, vitamin B12 is in cow's milk, yogurt, cheese, and eggs. B12 is an added supplement to many breakfast cereals.

Vitamin D is available by getting 10 to 30 minutes of sunlight daily. The amount needed depends upon season, skin color, and amount of skin surface exposed to sun. Those with dark skin need as much as 30 minutes of sun per day. Or a supplement of Vitamin D is necessary for those in Northern areas of the country such as Alaska, or those confined indoors such as with elderly or the sick. Supplement with five micrograms of vitamin D for people over 25 and 10 micrograms for those under 25 years of age, or pregnant and lactating, or those in Northern latitudes with little sunlight, or those confined to indoors.

11. Drink plenty of water daily—six to eight cups minimum.

Drink six to eight cups of water daily. If you are not a water drinker, try adding fresh squeezed lemon or lime as a great flavor enhancer. This provides an additional source of vitamin C. Herb tea is another great flavor enhancer to water.

12. Use fresh garlic and onion along with herbs and spices as flavor enhancers instead of salt, sugars, and fats.

"The greater number . . . suffer because of their own wrong course of action. They disregard the principles of health by their habits of eating, drinking, dressing, and working. Their transgression of nature's laws produces the sure result; and when sickness comes upon them, many do not credit their suffering to the true cause, but murmur against God because of their afflictions. But God is not responsible for the suffering that follows disregard of natural law"

(The Ministry of Healing, p. 234).

"Let your food be your medicine" (Hippocrates).

"A merry heart doeth good like a medicine"
(Proverbs 17:22).

FLAVOR ENHANCER GROUP:
*Essential oils, vegetable fats
sweetners, salt, herbs and spices*
Eat Sparingly

CALCIUM GROUP:
*Low-fat or non-fat, milk,
yogurt,soymilk, and
fortified alternative group*
4-6 Servings

PLANT-BASED PROTEIN GROUP:
*Legume, nut, seed, and meat alterna-
tive group*
5-9 Servings

VEGETABLE GROUP:
3-5 Servings

FRUIT GROUP:
2-4 Servings

GRAIN GROUP:
*Whole grain
bread, cereal,
pasta, and rice*
6-11 Servings

Illustration by Merle Poirier   © The Health Connection, 1994 PRINTED IN USA

PLANT-BASED FOOD PYRAMID

PLANNING HEALTH-PROMOTING MEALS

The following easy-to-follow, informative Meal Planning Guide will help you plan health-promoting, delicious meals. This Meal Planning Guide will help you build plant-based meals with or without the addition of low-fat dairy foods and eggs. Choose the plan that works for you. Begin the process toward better health by decreasing the animal-based foods and increasing the plant-based foods.

The steps toward building a great plant-based meal are to combine all of the following information about protein, calcium, iron, zinc, essential fatty acids, and fiber into a complete guide that helps us make our daily food choices.

The serving sizes that we have used are similar to the traditional Food Pyramid with the exception of the calcium and protein groups. In the pyramid, one cup of milk equals one serving. In the Plant-based Food Pyramid, a half cup of milk equals 1 serving. These are more appropriate serving sizes for the calcium-rich plant foods that can be used as milk alternatives. But the number of servings from the group is doubled. In the protein group (meat) in the traditional food pyramid, two to three servings from this group are recommended, but each serving is two to three ounces. This Plant-based Food Pyramid has changed the serving sizes to one-ounce serving sizes and increased the recommended servings per day to five to nine.

BREAD, CEREALS, RICE, POTATOES, AND PASTA

Intact grains mean less heart disease!

The grain group is the basis of the plant-based diet, contributing calories (energy), protein, B vitamins, and minerals. Whole grains are recommended because they add fiber and more of the vitamins and minerals. Remember to eat the majority of foods in their most natural state.

There is a big range of servings in the recommendations of the grains group, with six being the minimum

suggested amount. Six servings are suitable for those with lower caloric requirements such as those on a low-calorie diet or those with low-activity levels and the elderly. Teens and people who are more active will need more servings. Athletes with very high energy requirements may exceed 11 servings from this group.

GRAIN GROUP
Eat six to eleven servings daily.
(Whole grains are recommended.)

- Bread, 1 slice
- Small roll, biscuit, tortilla, scone
- 1 Large bun, bagel, large pita bread, or English muffin, 1/2
- Cereal, cooked, 1/2 cup
- Cereal, ready-to-eat, 1 ounce
- Pasta, rice, or other grain, cooked, 1/2 cup
- Pancake, waffle, or muffin, 1 small or 1/2 large
- Wheat germ, 2 tablespoons
- Crackers, 2 large or 4 small

The grain group is the primary source of complex carbohydrates in the diet, and this is the best fuel for our body for optimal endurance. Athletes with a high complex carbohydrate diet have as much as four times improved endurance versus a high-protein/high-fat diet. So energy and endurance come from the grain group.

Are carbohydrates a trigger food or not? Are carbohydrates a problem in weight gain? Are carbohydrates fattening. Should we avoid carbohydrates? Are you a sugar-buster?

Carbohydrates get their bad rap from their sugar content and how easily or rapidly the sugars are absorbed. But when you examine the carbohydrate foods, you will find that the sugar content of the more whole and intact foods, such as whole grains, whole vegetables, and whole fruits, is absorbed more slowly and is optimally used as energy for the body. Whole foods don't trigger the rapid blood sugar/insulin response seen with refined sugars and refined grains.

We see this in athletes, that complex carbohydrate loading is essential for endurance. The problem with carbohydrates is also that they are taken in excess. Carbohydrates and the sugar in them are essential for energy and endurance. Once you're full, any food you eat in excess becomes a bad choice. Overeating any good or bad food can cause weight gain! If our intake of refined simple carbohydrates is high, sugar cravings increase when the blood sugar levels reach low levels. This can also cause the weight gain that is so connected with carbohydrate foods.

Blood Sugar Regulation With Carbohydrates:

When you eat a snack full of sugars or refined carbohydrates, the resulting flood of insulin drives blood sugar levels too low. If there isn't any more digestible carbohydrate in the stomach, your body and brain start sending out hunger signals to make you look for more sugar even while the liver starts to release stored glycogen to regulate the sugar lows that result. So two things happen when the blood sugar drops: 1. Your liver responds by releasing more glucose to compensate for the rise in blood sugar. 2. You feel hungry and begin looking for more foods. **Whole grains and complex carbohydrates slow the absorption of sugar so the insulin levels don't rise and plunge, as they do with simple sugars and refined grains.**

It is easier to control our sugar cravings by avoiding or limiting our refined-sugar intake and refined carbohydrates. A meal chock-full of slowly digestible whole-grain carbohydrates slows down this glucose-insulin roller coaster because it takes longer to break down and absorb sugar molecules from whole grains—the insulin and blood sugar rise more slowly and peak at lower levels. This allows us to make it to the next meal without hunger and prevents snacking. For many people this is the cause for midmorning slump or midafternoon slump. If too many simple refined foods are in that meal, we will find one to two hours later we will be hungry again.

Factors That Modify Sugar Absorption From Carbohydrates

- The more water the grain has absorbed, the quicker the sugar absorption. Cooked potatoes are more easily digested than the starch molecules found in rice.
- How much the product is processed. Grinding wheat finely strips the protective fibrous coat, and sugar is attacked and absorbed more quickly. Regular oatmeal made of smashed oat grains absorbs sugar quicker than oats that are intact.
- How much fiber it contains. As indigestible fiber passes through the digestive tract it slows down the absorption of sugars, slowing the release of sugar into the system. So the more intact the fiber or less refined the grain or food, the slower the release of sugar.
- The amount of fruits, vegetables, fats, proteins, and other fibers eaten at the same time as sugar slows down sugar absorption and better regulates sugar absorption. Determines how quickly the sugar is absorbed. So eating foods with high glycemic index are slowed down from rapid sugar absorption by the addition of these foods.

What many do to offset this fast sugar absorption from refined carbohydrates is eat lots of fat and protein to offset the response and still do not increase the whole grains and complex carbohydrates. The healthiest solution to stop the blood sugar roller coaster is to increase whole grains, legumes, nuts and seeds, and whole fruits and vegetables and decrease refined carbohydrates. Supplementing with chromium is also helpful in regulating blood sugar.

"Those who ate whole wheat bread opposed to white bread, had a 40 percent decrease in risk of heart attack— even after accounting for differences in exercise habits, obesity, nut consumption, previous smoking history, and diabetes"

(Adventist Health Study).

FOCUS ON FIBER

Fiber is found only in plant food. Foods of animal origin contain no fiber. Refined grains and flours have been robbed of most of their original fiber content. Those switching to a plant-based diet will automatically see an increase in fiber.

We recommend eating foods in their most natural state—no white flour or white sugar. Remember, meat is a refined food—fiber never enters the bloodstream, but stays strictly in the digestive tract. So when you are eating meat, remember that the animal has excreted the fiber through the digestive tract. When the animal eats the grains and then we eat the animals, fiber is lost along with other key nutrients. This makes meat a processed, refined food—lacking fiber and many vitamins and phytochemicals that are needed for disease prevention.

When choosing fruits and vegetables, be sure they are fresh. Again, remember that it is better to eat the apple than drink the apple juice. Juice is a refined food!

What Is Fiber?

Fiber is a complex mixture of substances derived from the cell walls of plants. It is made up of long chains of glucose and glucose-like molecules joined together by bonds that our digestive enzymes cannot break down.

Two Types of Fiber

Soluble fiber—Mucilages, pectins, and gums are forms of soluble fiber found inside and around plant cells; they are the glue of the plant cells and help stop the cells from drying out. Soluble fiber dissolves or swells when put in water. Oats and oat bran contain gum, giving oatmeal its sticky consistency. Pectin is the substance in apples, berries, and oranges that causes jams, jellies, and marmalades to gel. It is especially helpful in lowering cholesterol and regulating blood sugar.

Insoluble fiber—Cellulose, hemicellulose, and lignin are structural components found throughout the plant kingdom. They do not generally dissolve in water, and so are called insoluble fiber. They attract and soak up water. Wheat bran is high in all three types of insoluble fiber. Legumes, seeds, root vegetables, and vegetables of the cabbage family contain substantial amounts of cellulose; as they age, their lignin content increases.

Sources of Fiber

Vegetables, fruits, legumes, whole grains, nuts, and seeds.

Fibers role in disease prevention:

● Is intestinal tract cleanser

● Prevents diverticulosis and hemorrhoids

● Protects against cancer; insoluble and soluble fiber have a role in decreasing our intestinal contact with carcinogens

● Has role in lowering blood cholesterol

● Regulates blood sugar for diabetics and nondiabetics

● Helps with weight control

How Much Fiber Do We Need?

Thirty to 40 grams of dietary fiber per day is recommended. The typical American diet contains 10 to 18 grams of fiber per day.

HOW TO GET YOUR DAILY FIBER FIX

● **Increase whole-grain products in place of refined breads, grains, and cereals**—contain two to three grams of fiber per half cup cooked grains or cereals. Look for 100 percent whole grains on the food labels. Opt for brown rice instead of white rice. The chewiest whole-grain breads were given highest satiety (feeling full) scores compared to white breads. You get more satisfaction with fewer calories.

● **Eat five or more servings of fruits or vegetables daily**—contain two to three grams of fiber per one cup fresh fruits or vegetables. Highest in fiber are berries, grapes, kiwifruit, pears, artichokes, kale, peas, and potatoes with skin.

● **Legumes are loaded with fiber**—six to eight grams of fiber per half-cup serving. Expand your bean repertoire: Try lentils, black beans, split peas, pinto beans, garbanzo beans, kidney beans, lima beans, navy beans, etc.

● **Nuts and seeds**—one ounce of nuts provides about three grams of fiber. Almonds contain four grams of fiber per serving. Seeds such as sesame, sunflower, and pumpkin are also fiber-rich. Calories add up quickly, so use nuts and seeds sparingly.

VEGETABLE GROUP

Vegetables are a good source of vitamin A (beta-carotine), vitamin C, vitamin K, minerals, fiber, and phytochemicals. Leafy green vegetables are good sources of folate; many are good sources of calcium as well. Vegetables in their natural state are cholesterol-free, low in fat, high in fiber, and nutrient-rich. Vegetables contain beta-carotine, which the body converts to vitamin A as needed. This is the safest form of vitamin A.

VEGETABLE GROUP
Eat three to five servings daily

- Vegetables, raw, 1 cup
- Vegetables, cooked, 1/2 cup
- Potatoes, yams, peas, and corn, cooked, 1/2 cup
- Vegetables, juice, 3/4 cup
- Salad, 1-2 cups

Eat two cups or two pieces of fresh or raw vegetables or fruits at every meal. This provides optimal nutrition to help you fill up on low-calorie foods to help with maintaining a healthy weight. Fill your plate with at least 50 percent colorful vegetables and fruits. Choose a variety of colors and types of vegetables for optimal nutrition.

The greatest nutrition deficiency in our country is lack of vegetables and fruit!

Types of Vegetables

Stems—asparagus and celery
Roots—carrots, turnips, and beets
Tubers—potatoes and yams
Flowers—broccoli and cauliflower
Seeds—peas and corn
Fruit of the plant—cucumbers, tomatoes, squash, eggplant, and okra

The tuber vegetables (potatoes and yams) and the seed vegetables (peas and corn) have traditionally been put in the bread group in the diabetic exchange. This is because their carbohydrate and calories are most similar to this group. The plant-based food pyramid puts potatoes, yams, peas, and corn in the vegetable group. Many weight-control diets ask you do avoid these foods because of their higher caloric content. We do not agree in avoiding these foods. We believe that if you are at your healthy weight you do not need to limit these foods. If you are trying to lose weight, just be sure that all five vegetable servings are not from this group alone.

You need to eat a variety of all types of vegetables. Potatoes, yams, corn, and peas bring simple and complex carbohydrates for energy, essential amino acids, minerals, vitamins, and fiber to your meals. Potatoes contain a good variety of essential amino acids, but in lower amounts so they are not considered a high-protein food. Potatoes and yams are good sources of nutrition and should not be avoided because of their high starch/sugar content. They are best eaten when included in a meal with whole grains, legumes, and vegetables. This will slow down the otherwise rapid sugar absorption the potato would have if eaten alone.

FRUIT GROUP

Fruits are a sweet, low-calorie source of vitamins A and C, folate, minerals, disease-fighting phytochemicals, and soluble fiber. Fruits are low in fat, cholesterol-free, high in fiber, and nutrient-rich. The only two exceptions: coconut and avocado. Fresh or frozen fruit is a must in a health-promoting diet. Choose the whole apple, skin and all, instead of applesauce or apple juice. Whole fresh fruits have more fiber than frozen juices or canned fruits.

FRUIT GROUP
Eat two to four servings daily

- Fruit (apple, banana, orange, peach, or citrus fruit), 1 medium
- Small fruit (apricot, plum, kiwi), 2 pieces
- Berries or fresh fruits, cut, 1/2 cup
- Fruit, fresh, frozen or cooked, 1/2 cup
- Fruit juice 3/4 cup (We recommend no more than a serving per day with meals.)

BERRY GOOD FOR YOU!

Berries are nutrient-rich powerhouses known for their disease-preventive qualities. We recommend one cup per day of fresh (or frozen unsweetened) whole berries daily!

They contain phytochemicals that fight against some cancers. Research has shown them to improve brain speed. They contain powerful antioxidant properties. It is not just one nutrient in the berry that is giving this health-promoting effect; therefore, research shows that supplementation of individual nutrients does not give the same disease-preventive qualities.

Remember, eating foods in their most natural state is the ideal for optimal nutrition.

Fruit is high in simple carbohydrates and can raise triglycerides in some people. Go easy on fruit juices and dehydrated fruits, such as raisins, apricots, and dates. They may be fat-free, but their concentrated natural sugar can add plenty of calories. This can raise blood sugar quickly. Eating the fruit in the fresh natural state combined with whole grains, legumes, nuts, or seeds can help regulate blood sugar. Eat whole fresh fruits for the slower release of sugar absorption. In addition, combine whole fresh fruits with whole grains, legumes, nuts and seeds to slow down the rapid rise in blood sugar that fruit alone can cause.

Diabetics and those with high triglycerides should eat whole fresh fruits with meals to decrease this effect. Diabetics need to be guided on how much whole fresh fruits they can tolerate by their home glucose monitoring. Whole fresh fruits are necessary for good nutrition and diabetics should try to include as many as they can tolerate. Eating these foods with their meals can typically increase the amount of fresh fruits they can tolerate.

Fresh fruits provide a wonderful alternative to a high-calorie dessert!

CALCIUM GROUP

How much calcium is needed?

Calcium is an important mineral needed for bones, teeth, muscle contraction and relaxation, blood clotting, transmission of nerve impulses, buffering acidity in the body, and the absorption of vitamin B12. 99 percent of the calcium in the body is found in bones and teeth. The U.S. Recommended Daily Allowances (RDA) for calcium is 1,200 milligrams per day for ages 11to 24 years and 800 milligrams for adults over 24 years.

What about milk—is it the best source of calcium?

Milk is a source of calcium and is traditionally marketed as the best source. However, adequate sources of calcium can be obtained from plant foods without milk and the saturated fats and cholesterol that come with the milk. Milk is also an animal food that is processed—lacking fiber and many vitamins, minerals, and phytochemicals that were in the original energy source—the plant! Much of the population is also lactose intolerant. There is concern about other unwanted chemicals or biological factors in milk—antibiotic residue, bacteria, hormones, and other contaminants. Dairy

◆ ◆ ◆ ◆ ◆ ◆ ◆ ◆ ◆ ◆ ◆ ◆ ◆ ◆ ◆ ◆ ◆ ◆

products are not necessary for bone health, based on the current nutrition research.

CALCIUM-RICH FOODS
Eat four to six servings daily

(Teens, young adults to age 24 years, pregnant and lactating women: six to eight servings)

Note: Many foods in this group count as servings from other groups as well.

- Soy or tofu milk, 1/2 cup
- Milk or yogurt 1/2 cup
- Cottage cheese, nonfat, 1/4 cup
- Tofu made with calcium, 1/2 cup
- Almonds, roasted, 20-22
- Nut butter, 2 tablespoons
- Legumes/beans, cooked, 1 cup
- Green vegetables (broccoli, kale, collards, Chinese cabbage, bok choy, okra), cooked, 1 cup
- Blackstrap molasses, 1 tablespoon
- Figs, dried, 5

Milk has been found to be a possible contributor to Type I diabetes if given to children at a young age (Diabetes Care January, 2002).

In a plant-based diet, almost every plant food eaten contributes to the total calcium intake averaging 500 to 1,000 milligrams per day. Studies show that those on plant diets have similar bone mineralization to that of omnivores. Certain plant leaves and flowers (green vegetables) are some of the best calcium sources around.

Research shows that the countries with the highest calcium intake from dairy foods tend to have higher hip fracture rates. (Statistics below are based on 100,000 women studied.)

- Sweden averages 1,300 milligrams of calcium per day and averages 90 hip fractures.
- U.S.A. averages 800 to 1000 milligrams of calcium per day and averages 60 hip fractures.
- Singapore averages 600 milligrams of calcium per day and averages 15 hip fractures.

Simply adding more calcium is not the answer. There are many factors that affect calcium levels. Oriental

countries have no dairy intake and high intakes of the oriental vegetables such as Oriental cabbage and bok choy. These are good sources of calcium and with two times the calcium absorption rate of milk. These Oriental countries have the least amount of hip fractures.

"Most studies of dairy food intake and bone health provided inconclusive results"

(American Journal of Clinical Nutrition, 2000).

"Elderly women with high dietary ratio of animal to vegetable protein intake have more rapid femoral neck bone loss and a greater risk of hip fracture than do those with a low ratio. This suggests that an increase in vegetable protein intake and decrease in animal protein intake may decrease bone loss and the risk of hip fracture"

(American Journal of Clinical Nutrition, 2001).

The Osteoporosis Solution

Simple calcium intake does not correlate with stronger bones. Calcium is very important in strong bones, but it may be that many other necessary nutrients and lifestyle factors all together are what is important in preventing osteoporosis.

Bone-friendly Vitamins and Minerals

Vitamin K—Higher vitamin K correlates with stronger bones and fewer bone fractures. Vitamin K is known for its blood-clotting effect, it also is required by osteoblasts—the bone-building cells—to produce proteins found in bone. Do not add more vitamin K if you are on blood-thinning medication without consulting with your doctor. The medication can be adjusted if your intake of vitamin K is consistently high. *Sources: Broccoli, brussels sprouts, cauliflower, chickpeas (garbanzo), dark leafy vegetables, kale, seeds, vegetable oils (olive, canola), dairy products, and eggs.* Nurses' Health Study and the Framingham osteoporosis study show protective effects of vitamin K with 90 to 250 micrograms per day intake. The least hip fractures were associated with higher consumptions of dark leafy greens.

CALCIUM-CONTENT OF FOODS

ITEM	SERVING SIZE	GRAMS OF CALCIUM (mg.)
Nori Seaweed	1/2 cup	600
Sesame seeds	1/4 cup	500
Milk, non fat	1/2 cup*	150
Milk, 2 percent	1/2 cup*	150
Milk, whole	1/2 cup*	150
Fortified nondairy beverage	1/2 cup*	125-250+
Unfortified nondairy beverage	1/2 cup*	5-95+
Yogurt, nonfat, plain	1/2 cup*	135-225
Cottage cheese, 4 percent fat	1/4 cup	150
Mozzarella cheese, part-skim	1/4 cup	150
Tofu (with calcium)	1/2 cup	200-300+
Sesame seeds	2-3 tablespoons	175-250
Broccoli, cooked	1 cup	178
Okra, frozen, cooked	1 cup	176
Blackstrap molasses	1 Tbsp	172
Chinese cabbage, cooked	1 cup	158
Collard greens, cooked	1 cup	148
Figs, dried	5 medium	135
Orange Juice, calcium-fortified	1/2 cup	100-150+
Mustard Greens, cooked	1 cup	100
Kale, cooked	1 cup	94
Almonds, roasted	20	75
Beans, dried, cooked	1/2 cup	40-80
Sweet potatoes, cooked	1/2 cup	88
Orange, fresh	1 medium	56
Tortillas, calcium-fortified	1 piece	20-150+

*Please note that we used 1/2-cup portions for milk, soy milks, and yogurts because this is the amounts most typically consumed at one meal for adults.

+Please read label for specific calcium content for these foods.

◆ ◇ ◆ ◇ ◆ ◇ ◆ ◇ ◆ ◇ ◆ ◇ ◆ ◇ ◆ ◇ ◆ ◇ ◆ ◇ ◆ ◇ ◆

Vitamin C—Necessary for collagen production, which is the framework for bone building. *Sources: Fresh fruits (especially citrus) and vegetables.*

Vitamin D—An essential vitamin needed for calcium absorption and utilization. *Sources: Sunshine preferred source and other fortified foods.*

The following minerals are for good bone health, and a deficiency in any of them can lead to poor bone health.

Calcium—For sources, see table following.

Phosphorous—This mineral is a major component of bone, second to calcium. *Sources: nuts, seeds, vegetables, and fruits.*

Copper—*Sources: buckwheat, mushrooms, peanut butter, seeds and nuts, split peas, vegetable oils (sunflower, olive).*

Boron—*Sources: apples, beet greens, broccoli, cabbage, cherries, grapes, legumes, nuts, peaches, pears.*

CALCIUM ABSORPTION IN FOODS

PERCENTAGE ABSORBED

Vegetables, cooked	50-62
(broccoli, brussel sprouts, cauliflower, Chinese and green cabbage, kale, mustard greens, turnip greens)	
Fortified tofu/soy milk, orange juice, fruit punch	52
Milk and Yogurt	32
Tofu (calcium set)	31
Soy	30
Sweet potatoes	22
Almonds, sesame seeds	21
(roasted nuts more absorbable)	
Beans, cooked (pinto, small red, white)	21-26
(soaking beans, sprouting seeds and legumes increase calcium absorption)	
Spinach (cooked), beet greens, Swiss chard, rhubarb	5

Silicon—*Sources: asparagus, cabbage, cucumbers, dandelion greens, lettuce, mustard greens, olives, parsnips, radishes, white onion, whole grains (rice and oats).*

Manganese—*Sources: whole grains, legumes, and nuts.*

Magnesium—*Sources: brown rice, buckwheat, corn, dandelion greens, dark green vegetables, legumes, nuts (almond, cashew, Brazil), rye, seeds (sunflower, sesame, pumpkin), wheat germ/bran, whole-grain cereals.*

Potassium—*Sources: fruits and vegetables.*

Zinc—*Sources: Brazil nuts, oats, peanuts, pecans, pumpkin seeds, rye, split peas.*

CALCIUM DEPLETERS!

Controlling the calcium loss may be more of a problem than actual calcium intake in preventing poor bone density.

Calcium can be depleted by the following:

- **High protein, especially animal protein**
- **High salt intake**
- **Alcohol intake**
- **Smoking**
- **High intakes of caffeinated beverages—coffee, tea, and some soft drinks**
- **Lack of sunshine**
- **Prolonged periods of inactivity**

In the average American diet, calcium absorption is only 30 to 50 percent of our dietary intake. Plant foods can be a powerhouse of calcium.

Low-oxalate vegetables with good calcium absorption include—Broccoli, kale, bok choy, mustard greens, Chinese and green cabbage, brussel sprouts, cauliflower, turnip greens, watercress

High-oxalate vegetables inhibit absorption of calcium—Spinach, beet greens, Swiss chard, rhubarb

Soy is high in both oxalate and phytate, yet soy products have relatively high calcium bioavailability. Common beans are rich in phytate, but have much less calcium bioavailability.

Should we add calcium supplementation to our diet?

The more calcium depleters that are in your life, the more you need supplementation. There is a role for calcium supplementation, but as with other supplements, they should not replace the need for real food. If calcium intake from foods is not sufficient, supplements can be useful. Those with good health appear to have no advantage in supplementing higher than recommended amounts of calcium.

The American Journal of Clinical Nutrition recommends many sources of high bioavailability foods along with calcium-fortified foods, especially for those on a plant-based diet. Calcium needs drop when one is on a totally plant-based diet. Those on a plant-based diet with or without the addition of dairy products who consume a variety of calcium-rich plant foods throughout the day will obtain sufficient calcium. **Remember, plant sources of calcium are green vegetables, tofu made with calcium, nuts, seeds, and blackstrap molasses.** Another source would be calcium fortified foods such as tofu or soy milk.

Nine Simple Steps to Strong Bones on a Plant-based Diet

1. Include three servings daily from the calcium group.
2. Eat dark green vegetables daily; include broccoli, kale, collards, bok choy, and Chinese cabbage. Learn delicious ways to prepare greens.
3. Use tofu made with calcium regularly. Remember, tofu is made from soybeans and takes on whatever flavor you add to it. Tofu is a great egg replacement in many recipes. The recipes in this book use tofu as an egg and cheese replacement.
4. Include sesame seeds and nuts as a part of your meals.
5. Try more Oriental favorites; nori seaweed is a great source of calcium and can be used for vegetable sushi or crumbled in salads, soups, or stir-fries.
6. Infants need breast milk, optimally, or if not available use calcium-fortified soy formula. Children need calcium-fortified soy or tofu milk.
7. Avoid high intakes of salt, alcohol, excess caffeine, animal protein.
8. Increase weight-bearing activity. Exercise is a prime bone strengthener; walking, jogging, and other weight-bearing exercise are essential for lifelong bone health.
9. Get 20 to 30 minutes of sunshine daily.

HIGH-PROTEIN PLANT-BASED FOOD GROUP

Beans, peas, and lentils are the protein powerhouses of the food guide pyramid. They contain iron, zinc, calcium, and a range of B vitamins, and both soluble and insoluble fiber.

Go Nuts!

Next time you find yourself lingering near a bowl of mixed nuts or seeds, swipe another small handful. Harvard University researchers reported in the November 27, 2002, issue of *Journal of the American Medical Association* that nuts and legumes can boost your health.

Research on 84,000 women over a 16-year period shows that eating five or more one-ounce servings of nuts per week lowered participants' risk for Type II diabetes and heart disease.

Nuts and seeds provide protein as well as being high in plant-based fats. They are good sources of the essential fatty acids. Almonds and sesame seeds are good sources of calcium. Cashews are a good source of zinc. Nuts and seed butters are valuable in

PLANT-BASED PROTEIN GROUP
Legumes, Beans, Peas, nuts, Seeds, Eggs
Eat five to nine servings (depending on body size).
(Each serving contains seven grams of protein.)

(Pregnant and lactating women need an extra one to two servings above normal intake.) Note: For increased iron absorption, eat vitamin C source at the same time.

- Legumes (beans, lentils, split peas, soybeans), cooked, 1/2 cup
- Tofu or tempeh, 1/2 cup
- Meat analogs (such as Tofu Burgers), 1 patty
- Nuts, 20-22
- Seeds, 1 ounce
- Nuts or seed butter, 2 tablespoons
- Egg, 1 large

the plant-based diet as a replacement for butter, margarine, or oils in recipes.

How much protein do I need?

Weight in pounds x 0.36 grams protein = grams of protein needed daily
or
Weight in kilograms x 0.8 grams protein = grams of protein needed daily

Calculate protein needs for adult weighing 150 pounds
150 pounds x 0.36 grams protein = 54 grams protein needed per day

Recommended amounts of protein: 10 to 15 percent of total calories should come from protein.

Where do we get our protein?

The typical American diet is built around meat, poultry, or fish, reflecting the deeply held beliefs that animal foods outrank plant-based foods in value. When the question is asked, "What's for supper tonight?" we most typically hear "hamburgers" or "chicken" or "steak." We don't usually hear "potatoes" or "broccoli" or "rice."

Do we need meat, poultry, and fish to meet our protein needs?

The following myths are based on research and thinking from years ago.

Three common beliefs regarding a meat-centered diet that are not true:

- I won't get enough protein without meat in my diet.
- I need animal protein to get the quality of protein needed.
- I won't get enough iron in my diet, and I may become anemic.

Current research concludes that there are no nutrients essential to human life found in meat, poultry or fish that are not also found in plant foods. Meat, poultry, and fish, however, are lacking many of the nutrients needed for human life that plant foods include. They are carbohydrate-deficient and fiber-free along with being high in cholesterol and fat. All the nutrients that are used to build animal and human bodies come from plants and microorganisms. Protein and iron required for muscle and blood are derived from grains, legumes, and vegetables. Even the bones and milk from cows, which are known for their high-calcium content, come from plant foods they eat. Animal protein is refined food. We need to decrease the refined foods in our diet!

Major Nutrients From the Protein Group

Whether your source of protein is from meat, poultry, fish or plant-based proteins, you need to be aware that the protein group is our main source for these four nutrients: **Protein, iron, zinc, and vitamin B12.**

Plant protein provides all the amino acids essential for life.

Protein is found in most foods with the exception of sugar, fats, and oils. Diets that provide enough calories and are based on a variety of plant-based foods will easily meet or exceed your protein requirements. For all types of diets, including diets with only plant-based foods, the average protein intake is more than one third higher than the recommended intake.

Advantages of Plant-based Protein Over Animal Protein

- Cholesterol-lowering
- Blood sugar-regulating
- Preserves bone density—less acidic, therefore preventing calcium loss common with animal protein.
- Improves circulation—contains high levels of arginine, an essential amino acid that protects against coronary artery disease and impotence.
- Helps with digestion on account of higher fiber.
- Less metabolic stress to kidneys because of less sulfur content that can tax the kidneys.
- Contains phytochemicals and other vital substances that prevent cancer and bone loss, strengthens the body in many other ways.
- Regulates hormones—Examples: Genistein and daidzein found in soybeans help modify hormones in

the body in a beneficial way and can help prevent bone loss and menopausal symptoms.

Plant-based protein food sources

Grains—wheat, oats, millet, and rice. Grains surprisingly are the source of almost half of the world's protein. Grains provide approximately 10 to 15 percent protein and are low in fat, and provide iron, zinc, B vitamins, and fiber.

Legumes—Plants that have seeds in pods: familiar legumes include lentils, peas, peanuts, soybeans, and chickpeas. Tofu, a traditional product of soybeans, has been called "the cow of China." It provides protein and iron, as does meat, and when made with calcium it is a good source of this mineral also.

Legumes are the protein powerhouses of the plant kingdom providing almost two times the protein content of cereal grains. Like meat, legumes are good sources of iron and zinc.

Legumes provide four distinct advantages over meat: they are cholesterol-free, very low in fat, abundant in fiber, and a significant source of calcium.

Frequent consumption of legumes has been found to reduce blood cholesterol levels and improve blood sugar control in diabetics.

Nuts and Seeds—PlantsNuts and seeds are high in fat (48 to 74 percent of total calories), but it's mostly unsaturated fat rich in oleic acid, a monounsaturated fat that's been linked to lowering low-density lipoproteins (LDLs, or "bad" cholesterol) and blood pressure, and providing protection against clogged arteries. Nut and seed

◆ ◆ ◆ ◆ ◆ ◆ ◆ ◆ ◆ ◆ ◆ ◆ ◆ ◆ ◆ ◆

butters can provide a good replacement for butter or margarine.

Nuts are a super source of protein and the amino acid arginine, a precursor to nitric acid, a substance that relaxes blood vessels and improves circulation by dilating blood vessels. Walnuts have the added benefit of substantial amounts of alpha-linolenic fatty acid, an omega-3 fatty acid that has been shown to protect against heart disease. Peanuts provide folate. Almonds are rich in vitamin E and calcium. Brazil nuts are extremely high in selenium, as well as quercetin and campferol, all of which have anti-cancer properties. Cashews are a good source of zinc.

Seeds do not have the research backing of nuts, but that doesn't mean they don't share the similar nutrition and possible health benefits. Sunflower seeds are particularly rich in vitamin E.

The Adventist Health Study demonstrated that eating nuts four to five times per week decreased the risk of heart attack by almost 50 percent.

Researchers at Pennsylvania State University reviewed 16 major studies and found that eating nuts regularly would significantly reduce the incidence of heart disease. The researchers concluded that eating an ounce of nuts more than five times per week could reduce the risk of heart disease by 25 to 39 percent.

The Physicians' Health Study concluded that of 22,000 men, those whose diets included the most nuts had the lowest risk of dying from heart disease.

The Nurses' Health Study of 86,000 women found that women who ate the most nuts—more than a half cup per week—were 35 percent less likely to develop heart disease or suffer a heart attack than women who ate nuts only once a week.

Nuts and seeds should be eaten in moderation. Include no more than a small handful a day if you are trying to decrease your body weight. If your diet is already sufficient in calories and fat, be careful that nuts and seeds take the place of other sources of calories; do not simply add them to your current daily intake, or you could gain weight.

Quick ways to add nuts and seeds:

- Toss two tablespoons of walnuts, almonds, or sunflower seeds on your salad or sandwich.
- Munch on a small handful of soy nuts instead of chips.
- Spread a thin layer of natural peanut butter (no hydrogenated fats added) instead of cream cheese on bagels.
- Add nuts or seeds to casseroles.
- Top quick breads with seeds.
- Stir two tablespoons of nuts and seeds into your breakfast yogurt or cereal.

Vegetables—We do not consider vegetables a high source of protein because most people eat so few vegetables at any given meal. However, the more plant-based foods in your diet, the greater the percentage of protein will come from these sources, since vegetables do contain 30 to 40 percent protein.

Iron in a Plant-based Diet

Most think of red meat as the source of iron. All the ingredients necessary for the formation of healthy blood, including iron, protein, vitamin C, and folic acid, are present in plant foods. After absorption, when iron actually reaches the cells and is used to manufacture hemoglobin for the blood, it is just as efficient whether its origin is steak or broccoli. The key difference between iron from steak or a veggie burger is the WAY the iron is absorbed.

Iron is critical for transporting oxygen from the lungs to cells throughout the body via hemoglobin. Iron is also present in muscle tissue, where it helps to store oxygen for future use. Small amounts are used in cell metabolism and fighting infection. Our bodies recycle iron, but we need to replace the small amounts lost—less than 1.5 milligrams per day. We absorb very little of the dietary iron that we consume. Because of this the recommendation for iron is 8 to 15 milligrams per day.

Premenopausal women need more iron than men, because of monthly blood loss.

Getting enough iron in your plant-based diet is not really so difficult.

- Eat iron-rich foods every day.
- Help your body absorb the iron you take in. Eat vitamin C–rich fruits and vegetables at meals.
- Avoid iron inhibitors at same meals as iron-rich foods.
- Have your iron blood levels checked with your annual exams to assure adequate levels.

Dietary Factors that Increase Iron Absorption

Foods rich in vitamin C works well with iron from plants. The amount of iron from cereal or breads can be doubled or tripled with the addition of a large orange or a glass of orange juice. One study showed an increase of six times greater iron absorption with the addition of papaya at the meal. Remember that fruits provide the maximum amount of vitamin C when raw.

Deficiency of Iron

Absorption of iron varies, depending on iron reserves in the body. If iron reserves are low, we may absorb twice as much iron from one meal.

Dietary Factors That Decrease Iron Absorption

- **Tannin-containing beverages**—tea, both black tea and Oriental green tea. Tea at breakfast was shown to cut the iron absorption in half.
- **A glass of milk or a serving of cheese** has been shown to decrease iron availability by as much as 50 percent.
- **Oxalates**—acids found in rhubarb, Swiss chard, and chocolate.

Broccoli, kale, and Oriental greens such as bok choy provide abundant available iron.

- **Phytates**—the storage form of phosphorus in seeds and associated with fiber in whole grains.
- **Soy products**—because of being high in oxalates and phytates. Tofu is a better source of iron because of the process the soybeans go through.

It is important to include vitamin-C-rich vegetables or fruit at most mealtimes for optimal absorption of iron from all sources, but especially critical for plant proteins.

ZINC

Role of Zinc

Zinc plays a central role in metabolism and enzyme functions. It is essential for reproduction, growth, sexual maturation, wound healing, and the immune system.

How much zinc do we need?

Consuming the recommended levels of zinc seems to be more of a challenge for both omnivores and vegetarians. Recommended levels of zinc—12 milligrams for women and 15 milligrams for men.

We can see from this information that meats, poultry, and fish can be safely removed from the diet and still meet the needs for protein, iron, and zinc.

SOURCES OF ZINC	
Nuts	(1 ounce provides 1.5 milligrams of zinc)
Flaxseed	(1/4 cup provides 2.62 milligrams of zinc)
Whole grains	(1/2 cup provides 0.6-2.1 milligrams of zinc)
Legumes	(1/2 cup provides 0.9-2.0 milligrams of zinc)
Vegetables	(1/2 cup provides 1.0 milligrams of zinc)
Fruits	(1 fruit provides 0.7 milligrams of zinc)
Milk and milk products	(1/2 cup provides 0.5 milligrams of zinc)
Nutritional yeast flakes	(1 tablespoon provides 1.0 milligram of zinc)
Egg(1 large provides	1.0 milligram of zinc)
Beef hamburger	(2 ounces provides 3.0 milligrams of zinc)

The common thought is that red meat is the best source of zinc. Many have been concerned how those on plant-based diets would get adequate zinc intake.

More Choices

FOOD SOURCES OF IRON

Food Sources of Iron:	Portion size	Amount of Iron in Milligrams
Legumes foods group		
Tofu, firm	1/2 cup	2
Lentils, cooked	1/2 cup	3.3
Beans, cooked	1/2 cup	2.2-2.6
Soy milk	1 cup	1-1.5
Nuts and seeds		
Sesame seeds	1 ounce	2.2
Tahini	2 tablespoons	2.7
Almond butter	2 tablespoons	1.2
Grains and cereal foods		
Cream of wheat (fortified)	3/4 cup	9-11
Fortified dry cereals	1 serving	4-18
Wheat germ	2 tablespoons	1.3
Whole-wheat bread	1 slice	1
Vegetables		
Wax beans, cooked	1/2 cup	3.1
Potato, with skin	1	2.8
Peas, raw, boiled, cooked	1/2 cup	1.2
Broccoli or bok choy, cooked	1/2 cup	1
Seaweeds		
Hijiki, dry	1/4 cup	6.4
Fruits		
Prunes, dried	10	2.1
Apricot halves, dried	10	1.7
Other foods		
Blackstrap molasses	1 tablespoons	3.2
Egg	1 large	1
Beef hamburger, lean, cooked	2 ounces	1.2

FATS AND ESSENTIAL OILS, SWEETENERS, SALTS, HERBS & SPICES

The tip of the Plant-based Food Pyramid is devoted to vegetable fats, essential oils, sweeteners, salt, herbs and spices.

FLAVOR ENHANCER GROUP
Vegetable fats and essential oil, sweeteners, salt, herbs and spices

Good Choices—Eat Modestly

Avocados—1/8 to 1/4 or (1-1 1/2 ounces)

Nuts—10-20

Seeds—2 tablespoons

Olives—

Essential oils—2.5 grams (1/2 teaspoon) omega-3 fatty acids daily

7-8 grams (1 1/2 teaspoons) omega-6 fatty acids daily

Flavor Enhancers:

Garlic, onions, leeks, chives

Spices and herbs (fresh is the best flavor, but dried also adds much flavor)—
    basil, dill, fennel, marjoram, mint, rosemary, oregano, sage, thyme,
    dill, cumin, parsley, cilantro, celery seed, anise, caraway, coriander,
    turmeric, curry, ginger, tarragon, green tea, licorice, flaxseed

Fruits for dessert

Bad Choices—Avoid or Limit

Animal fats/Saturated fats/High-cholesterol foods
    lard, butter, sour cream, cream, cream cheese, cheese, meat, poultry

Fried foods—french fries, deep fried foods, doughnuts

Oxidized or rancid Fats—Fried fats, stale foods, oils that have not been stored
    properly

Hydrogenated/Trans-fatty acids—Margarine, vegetable shortening, processed
    foods

Adding excess salt

Processed, pickled and cured foods

White flour/White sugars

This part of the pyramid is where we find the flavor enhancers for our foods. How can we add flavor to our meals and not increase our risk for disease? We will explore the good choices of foods in this group that will enhance flavor and enhance our health.

SWEETENERS:

Concentrated sugar is a source of simple, refined carbohydrates. It is high in calories and nutrient-poor. High intakes of refined sugars causes rapid absorption of sugar—rapid rise and fall of blood sugar levels causing hunger one to two hours after intake. Also, high sugar intake can raise triglyceride levels and excess is converted to fat. High sugar in the meals can also lead to tooth decay. Minimize your intake of concentrated sugar.

The best sweets come packaged in nature as fruits. Use fruits for satisfying your sweet tooth! Use fruit juices to replace sugary syrups and sauces,. Use more whole foods like fruits that are a natural source of sugar. When using fruits as a refined sugar replacement, remember to package even these fruits with other whole foods to slow down the blood sugar absorption rate.

SALT

Limit high-salt foods. Excess salty foods can contribute to hypertension or fluid retention, and can deplete calcium. Watch for salt in salty snack foods such as chips and crackers, and many prepared foods, pickled foods, and condiments. Use more of the natural flavor enhancers such as herbs and spices in place of salt. These foods will enhance the flavor and enhance your health.

FLAVOR ENHANCERS

(Extranutritional Components in Foods)

Many flavor enhancers contain phytochemicals that contain anticarcinogens. They either protect against cancer by inhibiting tumor formation by suppressing or slowing the cancer cell growth and/or preventing oxidative damage involved in the creation and growth of carcinogens. This results in lowering the risk of cancer. Other phytochemicals are known for their protective role in relation to coronary artery disease.

These flavor enhancers increase the flavor of our foods and at the same time increase the nutritional value of our meals, increasing our food's ability to fight disease. Salt and refined sugars enhance flavor, but also increase the risk of disease.

FOOD SOURCES OF FLAVOR ENHANCERS

Onions, garlic, leeks, chives—The component called allyl sulfur found in allium vegetables damages cancer cells and slows or prevents their growth. Garlic has been shown to lower blood pressure or play protective roles in relation to coronary artery disease.

Herbs and spices—Turmeric and curries with their characteristic yellow color act as an antioxidant. Dill, caraway, turmeric, and curries suppress the growth of cancer cells. Other herbs and spices can protect against cancer and heart disease, such as basil, oregano, rosemary, sage, thyme, cumin, parsley, cilantro, celery seed, anise, coriander, ginger, tarragon, green tea, licorice, flaxseed, fennel, marjoram, mint.

Fresh herbs provide the richest flavor, but if they are not available, use dried herbs that are as fresh as possible and store in refrigerator or freezer to preserve flavor.

Phytochemicals in Fruits, Vegetables, and Flavor Enhanceres.

Beta-carotene contributes a strong yellow pigment to the orange, red, green, and yellow vegetables, fruits, and herbs you see in every produce stand. In your body, this same beta-carotene acts as a scavenger of free radicals.

FATS AND ESSENTIAL OILS

Favor monounsaturated fats for the fat in your diet: olives, nuts, seeds, avocados, canola oil, olive oil.

These foods provide the essential fatty acids and promote health when eaten in moderation. Monounsaturated fats lower the low-density lipoproteins (LDL), or bad cholesterol, while maintaining the high-density lipoprotein (HDL) or good cholesterol. This protects against coronary artery disease.

Limit hydrogenated fats, partially hydrogenated, and trans-fatty acids: margarine, vegetable shortening, processed foods—check the label. Trans-fatty acids are found in processed foods that contain hydrogenated or partially hydrogenated oils, margarine, and vegetable shortening. Hydrogenation of fats is the chemical changing (or saturation) of vegetable oils to make them solid at room temperature and to improve the shelf life of processed foods. Research is showing trans-fatty acids to be as harmful as saturated fats in increasing our risk of disease.

Limit saturated fat intake: butter, lard, sour cream, cream cheese, cheese, dairy products, meat.

Saturated fats are found mostly in animal foods. Some plant foods have saturated fat such as the tropical oils—coconut and palm. We can easily identify saturated fats, since they are solid at room temperature. Saturated fats from animal sources increase cholesterol in the body by increasing low-density lipoproteins (LDL), which is the bad cholesterol. The LDLs increase our risk of coronary heart disease. The plant sources of saturated fats do not have this negative effect on our LDL levels.

Moderate intake of polyunsaturated fat intake: vegetable oils—corn, soy, safflower, sesame, etc.

Polyunsaturated fats are found in plant foods. These fats lower your cholesterol levels, both the low-density lipoproteins (LDL), or bad cholesterol, and the high-density lipoproteins (HDL), or good cholesterol. In the past this was the type of fat recommended as the best type of fat. This has changed because of the lowering effect on the HDL, or good cholesterol levels. Monounsaturated fats lower only the LDL, or bad cholesterol, maintaining the HDL, or good cholesterol levels. The most protective fats against coronary artery disease are the monounsaturated fats rather than the polyunsaturated fats.

Polyunsaturated fats tend to be liquid at room temperature (unless they contain a lot of hydrogenated oils) and are very susceptible to getting rancid. Antioxidants protect us from fat oxidation. Fruits and vegetables provide the needed antioxidants (beta-carotene, vitamins C and E, and selenium), particularly for individuals who are at high risk for disease such as smokers, people living in polluted areas, and those with a high family incidence of cancer or coronary artery disease.

One thing that all experts agree on is the importance of eating foods that are naturally rich sources of antioxidants such as fruits, vegetables, and whole grains every day.

Avoid oxidized or rancid fats; they are especially damaging to the body. Oxidation of fats can be caused from frying or exposure to air (oxygen) and/or sunlight for extended periods of time.

Even those on a plant-based diet can get too much fat, especially if full-fat dairy products, eggs, fried foods, and sweet baked goods such as pies and cakes are eaten regularly.

ESSENTIAL OILS

Essential fatty acids are the kind of fat we must have, but our bodies cannot manufacture.

The fatty acids that are essential for our bodies are:

OMEGA-3 FATTY ACID FAMILY--

Provides alpha-linolenic acid which is metabolized to eicosapentanoic acid (EPA) and docosahexaenoic acid (DHA).

Need .5 to 1 percent of daily calorie intake from omega-3 fatty acids or approximately 2.5 grams per day or 20 calories. Those on a plant-based diet need at least 1.0 percent because of the higher intake of omega-6s found in vegetable oils.

FOOD SOURCES OF OMEGA-3 FATTY ACIDS
Sources of omega-3s and the minimum amounts needed to meet your daily requirements. One serving per day.

- Flaxseed oil, 1/2 teaspoon
- Flaxseed, 2 teaspoon
- Canola or soybean oil, 1 tablespoon
- Walnuts, 3 tablespoons
- Firm tofu, 6 ounces
- Soybeans, cooked, 1 cup
- Dark leafy vegetables contain trace amounts (would need to consume 1 pound or 9 cups per day of raw broccoli or kale to meet minimum requirements)

OMEGA-6 FATTY ACID FAMILY--

Provides linoleic acid which is metabolized to gamma linolenic acid (GLA), which converts to arachidonic acid (AA).

Three percent of daily calories should come from omega-6 fatty acids or approximately seven grams or 60 calories (1.5 teaspoons of vegetable oil would provide this daily requirement).

Many recommend eating fish and fish oils to get the needed essential fatty acids—DHA and EPA. These fatty acids are needed for bodily functions. There are direct food sources of DHA and EPA in fish, fish oils, and other seafoods. Small amounts are also found in egg yolks.

FOOD SOURCES OF OMEGA-6 FATTY ACIDS

The omega-6s are found in seeds, nuts, and oils. You will have no problem getting enough omega-6 unless you are on a very low-fat diet (under 10 percent of calories from fat).

- Safflower, sunflower, corn, soybean, and walnut oils
- Sunflower, sesame, poppy, pumpkin seeds, and walnuts
- Wheat germ
- Many other plant and animal foods in small amounts

There are no direct plant sources of EPA and DHA. This is the basis for the common recommendation to include fish and fish oils in our diets. But **EPA and DHA are produced naturally in the body with adequate intake of omega-3 fatty acids. (See section on food sources for Omega-3 fatty acids.)**

We also can get direct food sources of gamma-linolenic acid (GLA) (a fatty acid metabolized in the body from omega-6 fatty acids that is necessary for the metabolism of arachidonic acid [AA]).

Food source—Primrose oil, borage oil, and black currant oils

Direct food sources of arachidonic acid (AA) (the end product of fatty acid metabolized from omega-6 fatty acids).

Food source—Animal fats

How do vegetarians get essential fatty acids from diet alone?

The essential fatty acids arachidonic acid, EPA, and DHA are readily produced by the body when we eat the recommended amounts of the plant foods that contain these two essential fatty acids alpha-linolenic acid (omega-3) and linoleic acid (omega-6). (See food sources for these fatty acids above.)

It is possible for those on a plant-based diet to get all the essential fatty acids without the use of supplementation and without consuming any animal foods when adequate intakes of omega-3 and omega-6 fatty acids are in our diet. (See food sources above.)

Foods that inhibit the body from producing DHA: The two classes of essential fatty acids compete for the desaturase enzymes that are necessary to produce the long chain polyunsaturated fatty acids (LCP)—arachidonic acid and DHA.

- High intakes of linoliec acid (omega-6) can inhibit conversion from omega-3 fatty acids to EPA and DHA
- High intake of trans-fatty acids (hydrogenated fats)
- High intake of processed foods or vegetable oils (corn, safflower, and sunflower, soybean, etc.)
- Low-fat diet too low to supply enough alpha-linolenic acid
- Alcohol

Note: vegetarians typically would have a higher intake of vegetable oils containing omega-6 fatty acids, which could slow down the conversion of DHA from the omega-3s. Vegetarians should be sure to get regular food sources of omega-3's to balance their higher intake of omega-6s.

When on a plant-based diet it can be easy to meet your essential fatty acid needs by just changing the type of cooking oil used—canola oil is a good source of omega-3 fatty acids and also high in monounsaturated fat.

Polyunsaturated fats have received praise and criticism regarding their effects on health and disease. Omega-6 fatty acids lower the blood cholesterol levels and omega-3 acids lower triglyceride levels and blood pressure. On the other hand, polyunsaturated fatty acids can go rancid very quickly, sometimes resulting in the formation of harmful chemicals that can contribute to disease processes.

Ensure the maximum health benefits of these valuable essential fatty acids by

- consuming appropriate amounts of the essential fatty acids—omega-3 and omega-6.
- storing these fats with care to prevent oxidation and rancidity. (Store oils in a airtight container, away from sunlight, and in a cool area—ideally the refrigerator.)
- avoiding fried fats.

For those on a plant-based diet we recommend using canola oil as your main cooking oil and adding other foods high in omega-3 fatty acids in your meals such as flax seed, walnuts, soybeans, wheat germ, etc. (See food sources of omega-3 fatty acids.)

VITAMIN B12

For those following a plant-based diet: Use fortified foods, such as soy milk or tofu milk and meat alternatives. Also consider a daily supplement to assure adequate daily intake of vitamin B12. We need an average of twp micrograms per day. For pregnancy or lactation, we need three micrograms per day.

Food Sources of Vitamin B12: Nutritional Yeast Flakes (Red Star T6635+)

Try adding these yeast flakes to your sandwiches, soups, salads, gravy, or sauces. It tastes great even on popcorn. This is not brewer's yeast, but is a yellow flake that has a cheesy taste. One tablespoon of nutritional yeast flakes provides one third of the daily requirement of B12.

VITAMIN D

Requirements are met by a short walk in the sunlight 20 to 30 minutes daily.

WATER

Drink six to eight glasses of water daily (this includes herb teas).

(Photo Copy for Use)

ASSESSING YOUR DIET

Plant-based Food Guide Score Sheet

Grain Products *(6-11 servings)* ❑ ❑ ❑ ❑ ❑ ❑ ❑ ❑ ❑ ❑ ❑

Vegetables *(3-5 servings)* ❑ ❑ ❑ ❑ ❑

Fruit *(2-4 servings)* ❑ ❑ ❑ ❑

Protein Group *(5-9 servings)* ❑ ❑ ❑ ❑ ❑ ❑ ❑ ❑ ❑

Calcium Group *(4-6 servings)* ❑ ❑ ❑ ❑ ❑ ❑

Omega-3 Fatty-acids *(1 serving)* ❑

Vitamin B12 *(1 serving)* ❑

Vitamin D *(20-30 minutes sunlight daily)* ❑

Water *(6-8 glasses, 8oz. each)* ❑ ❑ ❑ ❑ ❑ ❑ ❑ ❑

Use this food guide score sheet to check off your daily servings from each food group. This assures getting the nutrients needed per day for an optimal diet. This page can be photo copied and used as your daily reminder.

THE EVIDENCE IS IN—WHAT IS THE DIET OF CHOICE

The Evidence Is in—What Is the Diet of Choice?

The evidence points directly to a plant-based or near plant-based diet as the choice in prevention of chronic degenerative disease. A plant-based diet is a real health advantage. The evidence is strong!

"A considerable body of scientific data suggests positive relationships between vegetarian lifestyles and risk reduction for several chronic diseases, such as obesity, coronary artery disease, hypertension, diabetes mellitus, colon cancer, and other types"

(American Diabetic Association).

As we learn more about nutrition, we find more reasons to eat plant-based whole foods. Nature has packaged foods so that they provide more health supportive components than we may have realized in the past. Although the vitamin discovery era is complete, we are now finding new substances in foods that play an important role in the prevention of disease. These are phytochemicals found in such foods as garlic, onion, licorice, tofu, and cooking herbs. Scientists are also studying the role that trace minerals play in our overall being. These substances are all present in whole foods, but can be lost in the processing.

Remember, eating foods in their most natural state is our goal for better health.

"Returning to a predominantly plant-based diet may be the single most important thing we can do, as a group, for our health" (B. Stavric, PhD, <u>Patient Care</u>, Nov. 15, 1995, p. 36).

Famous people who believed in a plant-based diet

Ben Franklin, 1706-1790, "My refusing to eat flesh occasioned an inconvenience, and I was frequently chided for my singularity, but with this lighter repast I made the greater progress, for greater clearness of head and quicker comprehension."

Leonardo da Vinci, 1452-1519. "I have from an early age abjured the use of meat, and the time will come when men such as I will look on the murder of animals as they now look on the murder of men."

Albert Einstein, 1879-1955. "Nothing will benefit human health and increase the chances for survival of life on earth as much as the evolution to a vegetarian diet."

Other great advocates of plant-based diet: Plato, Socrates, Plotinus, Plutarch, Newton, Voltaire, Shelly, Darwin, Emerson, and Shaw, to name a few. It took great courage for these people to become advocates of vegetarianism in their times.

Dr. Dean Ornish presented evidence for the reversal of artherosclerosis through a combination of diet and lifestyle changes. He made a case for vegetarianism. Other outspoken physician-writers, including Dr. John McDougall and Dr. Benjamin Spock, have persuaded people to remove meat and milk from their diets.

"Fruits, grains, and vegetables, prepared in a simple way, . . . make. . . the most healthful diet" (*Testimony Studies on Diet and Foods,* p. 130).

"The diet appointed man in the beginning did not include animal food. Not till after the Flood, when every green thing on the earth had been destroyed, did man receive permission to eat flesh"

(The Ministry of Healing, p. 311).

"No one thing over which we have control exerts so marked an influence upon our physical prosperity as the food we eat" (Mrs. E. E. Kellogg, *Science in the Kitchen* [1892], p. 21).

God—"See, I have given you every herb that yields seed which is on the face of all the earth, and every tree whose fruit yields seed; to you it shall be for food" (Genesis 1:29, NKJV).

Breakfast

Breakfast Burritos

Belgian Waffles

Apricot Sauce

Cholesterol-free Pancakes

Apple Pancakes

Low-Fat Granola

Cheryl's Almond Granola

Breakfast Shakes:

Pineapple-Banana

Peach-Berry-Banana Fruit

Breakfast Scones With Fruit

Butter and Fruit Platter:

Almond-Oat Scones

Currant-Sesame Scones

Red Berry Spread

Peach or Apricot Butter

Five-Grain Cooked Cereal

Quick-cooking Seven-Grain Cereal

Fresh Fruit Sauce

Muesli-Nut Fruit Salad

BREAKFAST BURRITOS

1 ½	pounds thin-skinned potatoes
6	flour tortillas (10 inches wide)
1	red pepper, chopped (optional)
½	teaspoon garlic powder
2	cups firm tofu *or* 16 egg whites
½	teaspoon McKay's Chicken-Style Seasoning
1 ½	cup Thick and Chunky Salsa *(p. 139)* *or* purchased salsa
½	cup Tofu Sour Cream *(p. 136)* *or* low-fat sour cream
⅓	cup green onion, sliced thin

1. Peel potatoes, halve lengthwise, and cut crosswise into ⅓-inch-thick slices. Place in 2- to 3-quart pan with water to cover and bring to a boil over high heat. Reduce heat and simmer, covered, until tender when pierced. Drain.

2. Seal tortillas in foil and warm in a 350°F oven until hot, about 10 minutes.

3. Place cooked potatoes and chopped red peppers in a nonstick skillet, sprayed with nonstick cooking spray, and cook until lightly browned, about 10 minutes. Season with garlic powder and salt, if desired. Keep warm.

4. Chop tofu and sauté in nonstick skillet sprayed with nonstick cooking spray. Add ½ teaspoon garlic powder and 1 teaspoon McKay's Chicken-Style Seasoning, or to desired taste. Keep warm. (If using egg whites, beat them in a small bowl. Stir over medium heat in nonstick skillet until set. Add just the garlic powder and salt, if desired, to taste.)

5. Assembly: Lay tortillas flat. Toward one edge of each, fill equally with potatoes and tofu or egg mixture, and top with 2 tablespoons of the reserved warm chili sauce. Fold over sides and roll up tightly to enclose. Place each on a rimmed, ovenproof plate, and ladle warm Thick and Chunky Salsa on top. If the burrito needs to be warmed, place in oven at 350°F for 2 to 3 minutes until warm.

6. For a special garnishing touch, try putting the Tofu Sour Cream or low-fat sour cream in a small unpleated, heavy-duty plastic bag. Seal, then snip off a small corner of bag. Squeeze squiggles of sour cream over hot burritos. Sprinkle with green onions. Serve immediately.

Makes 6 burritos
Prep. time: 20 minutes
Cooking time: 10 minutes

MENU PLANNING TIPS

This delicious Mexican Breakfast Burrito tastes great stuffed full of vegetables and the tofu or egg white filling. Try this unique low-fat breakfast for a change at your next Sunday morning brunch. For quicker last-minute preparation, you can use a purchased salsa that you warm.

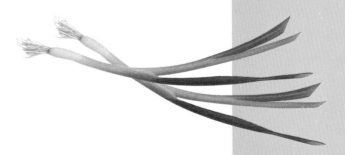

BELGIAN WAFFLES

10	ounces tofu, firm
1-2	cups tofu *or* soy *or* low-fat milk
2	tablespoons canola oil
2	tablespoons honey *or* sugar
1	teaspoon lemon juice
1	teaspoon pure vanilla extract
³/₄	cup whole-wheat flour, sifted
³/₄	cup all-purpose flour, sifted
1	teaspoon baking powder
¹/₂	teaspoon baking soda
³/₄	teaspoon salt
2	cups Apricot Sauce (recipe following)
1	banana, sliced
¹/₂	cup pecans

1. Preheat waffle iron.
2. Place tofu or 1 cup milk, oil, honey or sugar, lemon juice, and vanilla extract in blender and blend until smooth.
3. Sift flour, baking powder, baking soda, and salt.
4. Fold liquid ingredients into the sifted dry ingredients and mix. Add chopped nuts to batter, if desired, or use to garnish. (If using firm tofu [which has less moisture], the waffle batter could be too thick. Thin with additional milk until slightly thicker than pancake batter.)
5. Place amount of batter in waffle iron according to waffle iron directions. (Use any waffle iron for this recipe; however, a Belgian waffle iron, which takes about 4 minutes per waffle, makes a crisper waffle.) Cook until golden brown.
6. Top waffle or pancakes with the apricot sauce and place sliced bananas and nuts on top of sauce. Serve immediately.

APRICOT SAUCE

2	16-ounce cans pitted apricots, packed in fruit juice, undrained
¹/₄	teaspoon pure vanilla extract (optional)

1. Place apricots and vanilla extract in blender or food processor and blend to desired consistency. Blend until smooth or chunky, depending upon personal preference.
2. Place on waffle according to above recipe.

Serves 6
Prep. time: 5 minutes
Cooking time:
4 minutes per waffle

MENU PLANNING TIPS

These waffles can be served with any fruit topping and a nondairy whipped topping or Tofu Whipped Cream *(p. 136)*. The fruit topping provides a sweet taste with a lot less sugar and fewer calories than traditional maple syrup. It also provides one or two fruit exchanges to help in meeting the day's requirement for fruit. Strawberries are a great replacement for the apricot sauce. Also try topping the waffles with the Red Berry Spread *(p. 48)* or the Peach or Apricot Butter *(p. 49)*.

Serves 6
Prep. time: 5 minutes

MENU PLANNING TIPS

This sauce tastes great served over waffles, pancakes, French toast, and regular toast. You could also use peaches instead of apricots. Or blend 1 cup fresh fruit until smooth and add to 1 cup chopped fresh fruit.

CHOLESTEROL-FREE PANCAKES

Serves: 6
Prep. time: 5 minutes
Cooking time: 10 minutes

MENU PLANNING TIPS

Serve with fresh or canned fruit and nondairy whipped cream or Tofu Whipped Cream *(p. 136).* Add nuts or dried fruit for a variety in taste. Or try topping with the Red Berry Spread *(p. 48)* or the Peach or Apricot Butter *(p. 49).*

10	ounces tofu, firm
1	cup tofu *or* soy *or* low-fat milk
2	tablespoons canola oil
2	tablespoons honey *or* sugar
1	teaspoon lemon juice
1	teaspoon pure vanilla extract
³/₄	cup whole-wheat flour, sifted
³/₄	cup all-purpose flour, sifted
1	teaspoon baking powder
¹/₂	teaspoon baking soda
³/₄	teaspoon salt

1. Place all the wet ingredients in blender and blend until smooth.
2. Sift together all the dry ingredients.
3. Add the sifted dry ingredients to the blender mixture and mix until smooth.
4. Preheat nonstick skillet at medium heat.
5. Pour pancake batter into skillet to make the size pancakes desired. When the top of pancake begins to bubble, turn pancake over and cook until lightly browned.

APPLE PANCAKES

Makes 14 pancakes
Prep. time: 10 minutes
Cooking time: 10 minutes

MENU PLANNING TIPS

Serve with fresh fruit or fruit sauce of choice. Peanut butter and applesauce are a nice topping for these pancakes, or the apricot sauce with the waffle recipe.

1	cup whole-wheat flour
1	cup all-purpose flour
1	teaspoon baking soda
1	teaspoon baking powder
1	teaspoon ground cinnamon
¹/₂	teaspoon salt
2	cups tofu *or* soy *or* nonfat milk
2	teaspoons lemon juice
1	teaspoon pure vanilla extract
1	tablespoon honey
1	tablespoon molasses
1	tablespoon canola oil
¹/₂	cup soft tofu, blended smooth, *or* 4 egg whites
2	cups Granny Smith apples, finely chopped

1. Combine first six ingredients in large mixing bowl; stir well.
2. Combine milk of choice, lemon juice, vanilla, honey, molasses, oil, and tofu or egg whites in small bowl; stir well.
3. Add liquid mixture to flour mixture, stirring until smooth. Fold in apple. Let stand 5 minutes.
4. Spoon about ¹/₄ cup batter for each pancake onto a hot, nonstick griddle or nonstick skillet coated with cooking spray. Turn pancakes when tops are covered with bubbles and edges look cooked. Cook until lightly brown.

LOW-FAT GRANOLA

4	cups rolled oats
$^1/_2$ - $^3/_4$	cup walnuts, coarsely chopped
$^1/_4$	cup unsweetened coconut, shredded (optional)
$^1/_4$	cup sunflower **and/or** sesame seeds
$^1/_4$	cup brown sugar (optional, can increase honey by $^1/_4$ cup to substitute for brown sugar)
$^1/_4$	teaspoon salt (optional)
2	teaspoons ground cinnamon
$^3/_4$ - 1	cup apple juice concentrate, thawed
1	tablespoon vegetable oil (optional)
4	tablespoons honey
2	tablespoons pure vanilla extract
$^1/_2$	cup dried blueberries *or* dried cranberries
$^1/_3$	cup dates *or* raisins
$^1/_3$	cup thinly sliced dried apricots

1. Preheat oven to 300°F. In a large mixing bowl, stir together oats, nuts, coconut, seeds, brown sugar, salt, and cinnamon.

2. In a small bowl, mix apple juice concentrate, oil, honey, and vanilla extract. Use a whisk and whip honey into the juice mixture until totally dissolved. (Note: Use 1 cup of apple juice concentrate if you prefer a clumpier granola. If you like it more like individual pieces of oats, use $^3/_4$ cup juice.)

3. Drizzle juice mixture over the cereal and stir to coat evenly.

4. Spread the mixture onto a large baking sheet with sides. For even baking, be sure the granola is not more than 1 inch thick. Bake for 30 to 45 minutes, stirring every 5 to 7 minutes. Add the dried fruit and bake an additional 5 minutes. The granola should be crisp and golden. Do not overcook after adding the fruit to prevent the fruit from hardening. Sometimes I soak the dried fruit in hot water for 1 minute and then drain off the water just before adding to granola to keep the dried fruit moist and better blend the flavors with the granola. Let cool. Store granola in a sealed container in the refrigerator or freezer.

5. Serve the granola with tofu, soy, or nonfat milk and top with additional fresh fruit, if desired. Makes 5 cups.

Serves 10
Prep. time: 5 minutes
Cooking time: 30-45 minutes

MENU PLANNING TIPS

This granola has a great taste and contains no oil. So now you can eat granola and not get all those calories. The nuts and seeds are some of the best sources of the essential fatty acids and mono-unsaturated fat in our diet. Monounsaturated fat has been found to be the best type of fat to prevent heart disease. This cereal is also a great source of fiber, so eat it to your heart's content. Add fresh fruit to top this delicious breakfast cereal and serve with the milk of your choice to get a great breakfast that is perfect for those busy mornings. You can make extra granola and store in the freezer or refrigerator.

CHERYL'S ALMOND GRANOLA

Makes 5 cups
Prep. time: 5 minutes
Cooking time: 25 minutes

MENU PLANNING TIPS

This granola can be made with a small amount of oil, or without any oil. I like the crispy texture the oil gives the granola, but if you're trying to cut your fat to below 20 percent of the calories, delete the oil. The flavor is still the same with the oil-free version. One of my favorite breakfasts is a large bowl full of fresh chopped fruit, sprinkled with $\frac{1}{2}$ cup of either of these two granola recipes. You can top with the Tofu Whipped Cream *(p. 136)* or nonfat vanilla yogurt. This is a delicious low-fat breakfast that is sure to satisfy your taste buds and meet the daily nutrient recommendations for breakfast.

4	cups quick oats
$\frac{3}{4}$	cup toasted wheat germ
$\frac{1}{2}$	cup almonds, slivered
$\frac{1}{4}$	cup pecans, coarsely chopped
$\frac{1}{2}$	cup unsweetened coconut, shredded (optional)
$\frac{1}{2}$	teaspoon salt
$\frac{3}{4}$	cup frozen apple juice concentrate
5	tablespoons honey
2	tablespoons canola oil (optional)
1	tablespoon pure vanilla extract
$\frac{1}{4}$	teaspoon pure almond extract
$\frac{1}{2}$	cup dried fruit of choice (dates, raisins, apricots, blueberries, etc.), chopped *or* whole

1. Preheat oven to 300° F. In a large mixing bowl, combine the first six ingredients.

2. In a small mixing bowl, combine the liquid ingredients. I use a small whisk to dissolve the honey into the apple juice concentrate.

3. Drizzle the liquid mixture onto the dry granola and mix well to coat all the dry ingredients evenly. Spread uncooked granola onto large baking sheet with sides. Be sure the granola is not more than 1 inch thick so the granola bakes evenly.

4. Bake for 20 minutes, stirring every 5 to 7 minutes. Add the dried fruit and bake an additional 5 minutes. The granola should be crisp and golden. Do not overcook after adding the fruit to prevent the fruit from hardening. Sometimes I soak the dried fruit in hot water for 1 minute and then drain off the water just before adding to granola to keep the dried fruit moist and to blend the flavors better with the granola. Let cool. Store granola in a sealed container in the refrigerator or freezer.

5. Serve the granola with tofu, soy, or nonfat milk and top with additional fresh fruit, if desired. Makes 5 cups.

BREAKFAST SHAKES

PINEAPPLE-BANANA BREAKFAST SHAKE

Serves 4
Prep. time: 5-10 minutes

MENU PLANNING TIPS

You know you should eat breakfast. But what if you can't face solid food so early in the day? Try drinking your morning meal! These shakes are easy to make and easy to consume in the early morning and even taste great for a low-fat evening snack.

2	cups canned crushed pineapple, drained
$1\frac{1}{2}$	cups ice cubes
$1\frac{1}{3}$	cups Tofu Yogurt *(p. 136)* *or* nonfat yogurt
2	medium bananas, coarsely chopped
$\frac{1}{2}$	cup apricot nectar
$\frac{1}{4}$	cup toasted wheat germ
$\frac{1}{4}$	teaspoon pure vanilla extract (optional)
1	kiwifruit, peeled and sliced

1. In blender, combine the pineapple, ice cubes, yogurt of choice, bananas, apricot nectar, wheat germ, and vanilla extract. Blend until smooth.

2. Serve in tall glasses; garnish with kiwi slices.

PEACH-BERRY-BANANA FRUIT SHAKE

Prep. time:
5-10 minutes
Serves 4

2	cups Tofu Yogurt *(p. 136) or* nonfat vanilla yogurt
2	cups fresh orange juice
1	cup frozen banana slices
1	cup peaches
1/2	cup strawberries, coarsely chopped
1	tablespoon honey
1/2	teaspoon vanilla
2	cups ice cubes

In a blender, combine all ingredients. Blend on high speed until smooth and creamy.

BREAKFAST SCONES WITH FRUIT BUTTER AND FRUIT PLATTER

ALMOND-OAT SCONES

Prep. time: 20 minutes
Cooking time: 20 minutes
Makes 12 Scones

1½	cups unbleached flour
3	tablespoons brown sugar (optional, can replace with 3 tablespoons honey added to liquid ingredients)
2	teaspoons cream of tartar
1	teaspoon baking soda
¼	teaspoon salt
1⅓	cups quick oats
½	cup canola oil, chilled
½	teaspoon almond extract
5	tablespoons almonds, sliced and chopped fine
½	cup currants *or* unsweetened coconut, shredded
½	cup tofu *or* soy *or* nonfat milk
2	tablespoons additional milk of choice

MENU PLANNING TIPS

These scones combine the flavors of grains, nuts, and fruit to form delicious scones. They are perfect at breakfast with a fresh fruit platter or served with your afternoon tea. The Red Berry Spread or the Peach or Apricot Butter (recipes following) is the perfect topping for these scones.

1. Preheat oven to 375°F. Coat a large baking sheet with nonstick cooking spray.
2. Sift unbleached flour, cream of tartar, baking soda, and salt into mixing bowl. Mix quick oats and brown sugar into the sifted dry ingredients.
3. Combine oil and almond extract. If using honey for the sweetener, whisk it into the oil until it is dissolved.
4. Pour the oil mixture into the dry ingredients and toss with a fork until texture resembles coarse crumbs. Stir in the almonds and currants or coconut. Add ½ cup milk; stir to combine and moisten all the flour. Knead a few times to combine the ingredients thoroughly. (Avoid overkneading or the dough will have a tough texture.)
5. Working on a lightly floured board with well-floured hands, pat the dough to a circle about ½ inch thick. Using a 2½-inch fluted biscuit cutter, cut rounds from the dough and place them on the prepared baking sheet. Gather the scraps into a ball, pat them out, and cut more scones until all the dough has been used.
6. Place the scones on the baking sheet. Brush the tops of the scones with the remaining 2 teaspoons of milk. Bake for 12 to 15 minutes, or until golden. Transfer the scones to a wire rack. Serve warm or at room temperature. Serve with Red Berry Spread or Peach or Apricot Butter (recipes following).

Makes 12 Scones
Prep. time: 20 minutes
Cooking time: 20 minutes

CURRANT-SESAME SCONES

1⅓	cups unbleached flour
3	tablespoons brown sugar *(optional, can replace with 3 tablespoons honey whipped into oil)*
2	teaspoons cream of tartar
1	teaspoon baking soda
¼	teaspoon salt
3	tablespoons sesame seeds
1⅓	cups oat flour *or* replace with rolled oats blended to a powder
½	cup canola oil, chilled (replaces traditional margarine)
¼	teaspoon pure vanilla extract
½	cup currants
½	cup tofu *or* soy *or* nonfat milk
2	teaspoons additional milk of choice

1. Preheat oven to 375°F. Coat a large baking sheet with nonstick cooking spray.
2. Sift unbleached flour, cream of tartar, baking soda, and salt into mixing bowl.
3. Blend oats to a powder (if oat flour is not available). Add sesame seeds and oat flour to sifted mixture.
4. Combine oil and vanilla extract. If using honey for the sweetener, whisk it into the oil until it is dissolved.
5. Pour the oil mixture into the dry ingredients and toss with a fork until texture resembles coarse crumbs. Stir in the currants. Add ½ cup milk; stir to combine and moisten all the flour. Knead a few times to combine the ingredients thoroughly.
6. Working on a lightly floured board with well-floured hands, pat the dough to a circle about ½ inch thick. Using a 2½-inch fluted biscuit cutter, cut rounds from the dough and place them on the prepared baking sheet. Gather the scraps into a ball, pat them out, and cut more scones until all the dough has been used.
7. Place the scones on the baking sheet. Brush the tops of the scones with the remaining 2 teaspoons of milk.
8. Bake for 12 to 15 minutes, or until golden. Transfer the scones to a wire rack. Serve warm or at room temperature.

RED BERRY SPREAD

Makes 1 cup
Prep. time: 5 minutes
Cooking time: 30 minutes

1	cup fresh *or* thawed frozen whole strawberries
½	cup fresh *or* thawed frozen raspberries
1	tablespoon honey
2	teaspoons brown sugar (optional)
1	cinnamon stick
1	tablespoon grated lemon peel

1. In a 1-quart saucepan, combine all ingredients. Bring to a boil over medium heat. Reduce the heat to low. Simmer, stirring frequently, for 30 minutes, or until the mixture is thick. Remove and discard the cinnamon stick. If you choose to blend the berries for a smooth spread, it is best to blend before boiling.
2. Cool, then transfer to a bowl or jar. Store, tightly covered, in the refrigerator. Serve with scones.

MENU PLANNING TIPS

Red Berry Spread is good with scones, as well as with any other breakfast or brunch bread, pancake, or waffle. Blending the berries before cooking will give you a smooth spread. Cooking the whole berries gives you more of a fresh fruit jam taste. Any fresh fruit can be used in this spread. Be creative; try your favorite fruit combinations. You can also thicken this spread by adding a small amount of cornstarch if you need to speed up the process of thickening, or if you want to use juices in the spread. Add 1 teaspoon cornstarch per cup of liquid used and add to cold liquid before combining with other fruit.

PEACH OR APRICOT BUTTER

2	cups dried peaches *or* apricots
1	12-ounce can unsweetened frozen apple juice concentrate, undiluted
1½	cups water
1	teaspoon ground cinnamon (optional)

1. Soak dried peaches or apricots in apple juice concentrate overnight. For last-minute preparation, combine dried fruit and juice concentrate and bring to a boil, then simmer, covered, for approximately 10 minutes, or until fruit is softened. Let cool.
2. Blend softened fruit in blender or food processor until buttery smooth; add cinnamon if desired.
3. Serve with scones, or on toast. This is a very thick, spreadable mixture. This can also be used with waffles or pancakes, served with nondairy whipped topping.

Makes 4 cups
Prep. time: 5 minutes
Cooking time: 10 minutes

FIVE-GRAIN COOKED CEREAL

1	cup whole-grain oats
½	cup cracked wheat
½	cup whole-grain barley
½	cup cornmeal
½	cup millet
6	cups water
1	teaspoon salt
½	cup dried fruit (apricots, dates, raisins, blueberries, etc.)
½	cup tofu *or* soy *or* nonfat milk (optional)

1. Place all the ingredients in the Crock-Pot and cover. Cook on low; slow-cook 6 hours. If longer cooking time is necessary, add more water so the cereal does not dry out too much. If you cook the cereal on high, it can be done as soon as 3 hours. This recipe can be cut in half; just remember to follow the basic guidelines of one part grain to two parts water.
2. Serve with fresh fruit, fruit sauce of choice *(recipes in this breakfast section)*, *and/or* nondairy milk or nonfat milk.

Makes 6 cups
Prep. time: 5 minutes
Cooking time: 6 hours or overnight in Crock-Pot

MENU PLANNING TIPS
This is a great way to wake up to breakfast, already cooked. While you are sleeping, the Crock-Pot is slowly cooking these whole grains and releasing the wonderful flavors hidden within them. (Note: Use any combination of whole grains to equal 3 cups.)

QUICK-COOKING SEVEN-GRAIN CEREAL

3½	cups water
¼	teaspoon salt
1¾	cups rolled oats
¼	cup seven-grain cereal (the grains are crushed and sold as a mix)
¼-½	cup dried blueberries, raisins, *or* dates
¼	cup slivered almonds (optional)
½	cup tofu *or* soy *or* nonfat milk

1. Place water and salt in a medium-size pan; cover and bring to a boil.
2. Add oats and seven-grain cereal to boiling water. Return to a boil and then lower temperature and simmer, covered, for 10 minutes. Add dried fruit and nuts during the last 3 to 5 minutes of cooking.

Serves 4
Prep. time: 5 minutes
Cooking time: 10 minutes

MENU PLANNING TIPS
This cereal is a great way to get your fiber and B vitamins. Add milk of choice, and top with fresh fruit or fresh fruit sauce *(p. 43)*.

FRESH FRUIT SAUCE

2   cups fresh berries *or* fruit of choice

1/2 teaspoon pure vanilla extract

1. Place one-half of berries or fresh fruit of choice in blender and blend until smooth.
2. Add vanilla extract and chopped fresh fruit to blended fruit and mix well. Serve chilled or at room temperature.

Serves 4
Prep. time:
5-10 minutes

MENU PLANNING TIPS
Serve over pancakes, waffles, or toast.

MUESLI-NUT FRUIT SALAD

FRUIT SALAD:

1/2 cantaloupe, peeled and cut into 1-inch pieces

1   small apple, peeled, cored, and cut into bite-size pieces

1   mango, peeled and cut into chunks

1   banana, thinly sliced

2   peaches, coarsely chopped

5   strawberries, fresh *or* frozen, cut in slices

MUESLI-NUT TOPPING:

1/4 cup quick *or* rolled oats

1/4 cup unsalted cashews, almonds, pecans, *or* walnuts

2-4 tablespoons unsweetened, shredded coconut

1   tablespoon sesame seeds

1/8 teaspoon ground cinnamon

1/2 cup raisins, dried blueberries, *or* dates (optional)

2   cups Tofu Yogurt *(p. 136)* or nonfat yogurt

1. In a medium-size mixing bowl, combine the fruit.
2. In a food processor, combine the oats, nuts, coconut, sesame seeds, and cinnamon. Process with on/off turns until coarsely ground; do not overprocess or the mixture will become a paste. Sprinkle over the fruit.
3. Stir in the raisins, dates, dried blueberries, or dried fruit of choice. Serve topped with yogurt of choice.

Serves 1 or 2
Prep. time: 10 minutes

MENU PLANNING TIPS
This is an easy alternative to breakfast cereals, a great dieter's breakfast. Be sure to eat lots of this so that it will hold you till the next meal. Serve in a large salad bowl; it's a great way to eat a huge, satisfying breakfast and not feel guilty. You can use your favorite combination of fruit. This recipe is my favorite combination and the amount I eat almost every day for breakfast. I top my fruit with either this nut mixture, or I'll use one of the granolas from the breakfast section. Surprisingly, you'll find this will satisfy you for many hours.

Lunch

SANDWICHES

Grilled Vegetable Sandwich With
Creamy Herb Dressing

Roasted Vegetable Pitas With
Creamy Herb Dressing

Lentil Patties in Pita Pockets With
Creamy Cucumber Dressing

Italian-Style Vegetarian Hoagie

Oven-baked Seasoned Fries

Guilt-free Burgers

Toasted Bagels With Roasted Red
Pepper Spread

Garbanzo Bean Sandwiches

Mexican Chili Burgers

Oven-baked Mexi-Fries

GRILLED VEGETABLE SANDWICH WITH CREAMY HERB DRESSING

2   medium zucchini, cut lengthwise into ¼-inch oblong slices

1   medium red bell pepper, cut into 1-inch pieces

1   medium yellow bell pepper, cut into 1-inch pieces (optional)

1   large onion, cut into ½-inch slices

½   cup sun-dried tomatoes, soaked for 2 minutes in boiling water and chopped

2   garlic cloves, thinly sliced (optional)

4   6- to 8-inch sections of French bread

MARINADE:

¼   cup lemon juice

2   tablespoons olive oil

1-2   teaspoons light molasses (can substitute honey or sugar)

1   tablespoon fresh basil, chopped *or* 1 teaspoon dried basil

1   tablespoon fresh thyme *or* ½ teaspoon dried thyme (optional)

¼   teaspoon salt (optional)

1. Prepare Creamy Herb Dressing *(p. 138)* and refrigerate until serving time.
2. Prepare and cut vegetables. Rehydrate sun-dried tomatoes as directed in ingredient list.
3. Mix together all marinade ingredients.
4. In large bowl, toss together vegetables and marinade. If desired, you can let the vegetable mixture marinate for 2 hours in the refrigerator in a zip-top plastic bag, but this step is not necessary.
5. Grill or roast following these directions:

GRILLING:

Place vegetables in a wire grilling basket, coated with cooking spray. Prepare grill. Place grilling basket on grill rack; grill 5 minutes, basting occasionally with remaining marinade. Turn basket over; grill 2 minutes, basting occasionally. Cut the bread horizontally and brush with 3 tablespoons of the marinade. Place bread, cut side down, on grill rack and grill with the vegetables an additional 3 minutes, or until vegetables are tender and bread is toasted.

ROASTING OR BROILING:

Preheat oven to broil. Place vegetable mixture on a baking sheet and spread out thinly. Broil for 5 minutes; turn vegetable mixture and baste with more marinade if needed. Broil for an additional 5 minutes, or until vegetables are just tender and roasted. Remove vegetable mixture from the oven and put the bread, brushed with 3 tablespoons of marinade, under the broiler, toasting until lightly browned.

6. Spread Creamy Herb Dressing liberally on toasted sides of both pieces of bread. Top bottom piece with liberal amount of grilled or roasted vegetable mixture; top with other half of bread. Serve with side dish of creamy dressing for dipping and extra drizzling.

Serves 4
Prep. time: 10 minutes
Cooking time: 10 minutes

MENU PLANNING TIPS

This sandwich can be grilled or roasted. Directions are included for both techniques. The vegetable mixture makes a delicious full-meal sandwich, and the Creamy Herb Dressing enhances its flavor. Be sure the dressing isn't too thick, or it will overpower the taste of the vegetables. The consistency of French dressing is about right. A baked potato chip tastes great on the side of this sandwich and still maintains the theme of this low-fat, healthy menu. For dessert, add a fat-free sorbet purchased from the grocery store, or try a cool, refreshing fruit smoothie or sorbet from the dessert section of this book.

ROASTED VEGETABLE PITAS WITH CREAMY HERB DRESSING

1	cup yellow summer squash, cut in ½-inch diagonal slices
1	red pepper, cut into wedges
1	small onion, cut into eight wedges
2	garlic cloves, thinly sliced
1	large tomato, cut into eight wedges
½	cup spinach leaves, washed and torn into bite-size pieces (optional)
1½	teaspoons olive oil
1½	teaspoons fresh oregano, chopped, *or* ½ teaspoon dried oregano
1½	teaspoons fresh basil, chopped, *or* ½ teaspoon dried basil (optional)
¼	teaspoon salt (optional)
⅓	cup Creamy Herb Dressing *(p. 138)*
2-4	whole-wheat pita pocket halves

1. Prepare and cut vegetables.

2. Combine in mixing bowl all the above ingredients except the tomatoes and creamy dressing. Toss vegetable mixture to lightly glaze the vegetables with olive oil and herbs.

3. Spoon vegetable mixture onto a broiler pan or cookie sheet coated with nonstick cooking spray. Broil 5 minutes; add tomatoes and spinach leaves to vegetable mixture and stir. Baste with additional marinade and broil for 5 additional minutes, or until vegetables are just tender and lightly browned. Tomatoes and spinach should be just warmed; if you prefer the tomato softer, add with vegetable mixture at the beginning of the 10 minutes.

4. Prepare the Creamy Herb Dressing while the vegetables are broiling.

5. Divide vegetable mixture evenly between two pita halves. Drizzle 2 tablespoons creamy dressing over each pita sandwich. Serve.

Serves 2
Prep. time: 10 minutes
Cooking time: 10 minutes

MENU PLANNING TIPS
You can use eggplant, zucchini, and red, green, or yellow pepper in this vegetable mixture. Serve with baked potato wedges.

LENTIL PATTIES IN PITA POCKETS WITH CREAMY CUCUMBER DRESSING

Serves 6-8
Prep. time: 15 minutes
Cooking time: 30 minutes

MENU PLANNING TIPS

These delicious lentil patties have a unique flavor, similar to the seasoning in a falafel. I like to make these patties with leftover lentils from lentil soup or leftover rice. This saves time in preparation and is a good way to use leftovers creatively. Serve these patties in the pita pockets, or serve with rice or potatoes for a main meal. Any way you serve them, they are sure to be enjoyed by all. Garnish with chopped tomatoes or red peppers. Serve with carrots and celery sticks on the side.

6-8	whole-wheat pita pocket halves
1	cup Creamy Cucumber Dressing *(p. 138)*
16-24	Lentil Patties, 1$\frac{1}{2}$-inch diameter

1. Prepare Lentil Patties (recipe following).

2. Crumble Lentil Patties into pita pocket halves.

3. Top each pita pocket sandwich with 2 tablespoons Creamy Cucumber Dressing. Serve with side dish of dressing for extra drizzling.

LENTIL PATTIES

1$\frac{1}{4}$	cups uncooked lentils *or* 3 cups cooked lentils
1	small onion, chopped
$\frac{1}{2}$	cup tofu, soft, *or* four egg whites
2	garlic cloves, minced
$\frac{1}{2}$	teaspoon ground cumin
1	teaspoon sage
1	teaspoon garlic powder
$\frac{1}{4}$	teaspoon salt
$\frac{1}{8}$	teaspoon hot sauce (optional)
1	cup whole-grain rice, cooked
1	small carrot, shredded
$\frac{1}{2}$	cup cracker crumbs
$\frac{1}{2}$	cup pecans, chopped (optional, for texture)

1. Place lentils in 2-quart saucepan. Cover with water and bring to a boil over medium-high heat. Reduce heat to low. Simmer, covered, for 30 minutes or until lentils are tender; drain.

2. Line baking sheet with a double thickness of paper towels. Spoon cooked lentils onto the paper towels. Let stand about 20 minutes, or until lentils are cool and most of moisture has been absorbed.

3. In blender, combine half the cooked, drained lentils, onion, tofu or egg whites, garlic cloves, cumin, sage, garlic powder, salt, and hot sauce and blend until smooth. Mixture will be thick.

4. Place blended lentil mixture in mixing bowl and add rice, shredded carrots, cracker crumbs, and chopped pecans. Mix thoroughly. Add more cracker crumbs, if needed, to thicken patties.

5. Coat bottom of large skillet with small amount of canola oil or nonstick cooking spray. Place 2 rounded tablespoons full of lentil mixture in palm of hand; shape into patty. Repeat with remaining lentil mixture.

6. Place patties in skillet. Flatten to even thickness with spatula. Cook patties over medium heat for 6 to 7 minutes on each side until browned on both sides.

ITALIAN-STYLE VEGETARIAN HOAGIE

1	18- to 24-inch hoagie roll *(French bread also can be used for this)*
2½	tablespoons light olive oil
1-2	teaspoons dried oregano
	garlic powder to taste
	salt to taste (optional)
8	ounces Worthington Meatless Corned Beef **and/or** Smoked Turkey (optional)
2-3	large tomatoes, sliced thick
2	cucumbers, peeled and sliced lengthwise
4-5	cups head lettuce, shredded
1	large sweet red pepper, sliced thin
½	sweet onion, sliced in thin circles (optional)

1. Preheat oven to broil if toasting the bread. Cut the hoagie roll lengthwise and open it for assembly. Drizzle olive oil over both sides of bread, and then place top piece over bottom piece and lightly squeeze together to help evenly absorb the olive oil. Open roll with oiled sides up and sprinkle oregano, garlic powder, and salt over oil layer. Toast bread under broiler for 2 to 4 minutes, if you desire toasted bread.

2. Fold meatless corned beef and/or turkey slices in half and line bottom piece of the roll. Top with tomato slices, cucumbers, lettuce, sweet red peppers, and onions.

3. Drizzle vegetable layer with more olive oil and sprinkle with oregano, garlic powder, and salt, if desired. You can also use a low-fat Italian dressing to drizzle over vegetable mixture. Cover with top half of bread, cut (if using the long loaves), and serve.

OVEN-BAKED SEASONED FRIES

1½	pounds *or* seven medium baking potatoes, peeled and cut into thin strips
1	tablespoon canola *or* light olive oil
½	teaspoon garlic powder
¼-½	teaspoon paprika (optional)
¼	teaspoon salt (optional)

1. Preheat oven to 450°F.
2. Combine all ingredients in a bowl; toss well. Arrange the potatoes in a single layer on a baking sheet. Bake for 15 to 20 minutes, or until golden brown.

Serves 4
Prep. time: 10 minutes
Cook time: 5 minutes

MENU PLANNING TIPS
This Italian hoagie is perfect for a fast dinner, a quick-to-prepare picnic, or a party. I find it faster to assemble one long hoagie, versus making four separate ones, but you can assemble this great Italian filling into individual rolls or long rolls. Some bakeries make whole-wheat hoagie rolls, which increases your fiber intake for the day. You can enjoy the hoagie toasted or left cold. Either way, this hearty sandwich will be a hit. The oregano and olive oil seasoning give this vegetarian hoagie the Italian touch.

Serves 4
Prep. time: 10 minutes
Baking time: 15-20 minutes

MENU PLANNING TIPS
Serve these garlic-flavored oven fries with the Guilt-free Burger and any other vegetable dish. They add a unique twist to the traditional baked potato and have a quicker baking time. Be sure to use baking potatoes. Thin-skinned potatoes, which have a higher sugar content than baking potatoes, will burn on the outside before the inside is cooked, resulting in a soggy fry.

GUILT-FREE BURGERS

Makes 16 three-inch burgers
Prep. time: 15 minutes
Cooking time: 15 minutes

MENU PLANNING TIPS

Serve these delicious burger sandwiches on whole-wheat burger buns with Ranch Soy Mayonnaise *(p. 137)* or other dressing of choice, tomato slices, lettuce, and sliced onion. You can vary the flavor by adding different vegetables and dressings. Add Oven-Baked Seasoned Fries *(p. 57)* or baked potato chips for a light lunch or dinner.

1½	cups water
1	cup seven-grain cereal
¼	cup water
1	teaspoon McKay's Chicken-Style Seasoning *or* Chicken-like Seasoning *(p. 135)*
½	cup onions, chopped
½	cup carrots, shredded
½	cup zucchini, shredded (optional)
1	teaspoon dried thyme
2	cups cooked brown rice
10	ounces soft tofu *or* ½ cup egg whites *or* egg substitute
2-4	slices whole-wheat toast, crushed into crumbs *or* ½-1 cup cracker crumbs
¼	cup walnuts, chopped
1½	teaspoons garlic powder
1-2	teaspoons sage

1. In a small microwaveable bowl, combine 1½ cups of water with the seven-grain cereal. Cover and cook on high for 5 minutes. Grains should be softened. Let sit to cool while preparing the remaining ingredients.

2. In a large nonstick skillet over medium heat, stir together and heat the water and McKay's Chicken-Style Seasoning or Chicken-like Seasoning. Add the onions, carrots, zucchini, and thyme; cook, stirring frequently, for 4 to 5 minutes, or until the vegetables are tender and the liquid has evaporated.

3. In large mixing bowl, mix together the sautéed vegetables, softened grains, rice, tofu or egg whites, toasted bread crumbs, walnuts, garlic powder, and sage. Mix well. If mixture is too thin to form patties, add one to two slices of bread, crushed into crumbs, to thicken pattie mixture.

4. Shape into 3-inch diameter patties that are ½ to 1 inch in thickness.

5. Wash and dry the nonstick skillet. Spray with nonstick cooking spray and place it over medium heat. Add the patties and sauté for about 5 minutes per side, or until golden.

TOASTED BAGELS WITH ROASTED RED PEPPER SPREAD

8	ounces soft tofu, well drained and squeezed dry between paper towels
1	tablespoon tofu *or* soy *or* nonfat milk
1	tablespoon lemon juice
1	teaspoon honey
$\frac{1}{8}$	teaspoon salt
$\frac{1}{4}$	cup roasted sweet red peppers, chopped
$\frac{1}{4}$	cup cucumber, seeds removed, grated
2	tablespoons green onion, chopped
4	bagels, split in half
8	large tomato slices

1. Crumble the tofu into a food processor. Add the milk, lemon juice, honey and salt; process until smooth. Transfer to a small bowl.
2. Stir in the red peppers, cucumbers, and green onions. Cover and refrigerate for at least 1 hour.
3. To serve, toast the bagels. Spread with the red pepper-tofu mixture; top each half with a tomato slice.

Serves 4
Prep. time: 10 minutes
Cooking time: 5 minutes

MENU PLANNING TIPS
This toasted bagel makes a nice light lunch or dinner, and even works for breakfast.

GARBANZO BEAN SANDWICHES

1	can garbanzo beans (15-16 ounces), rinsed and drained
$\frac{1}{2}$	cup water
2	tablespoons fresh parsley, chopped
2	tablespoons walnuts, chopped
1	tablespoon onion, finely chopped
1	clove garlic, finely chopped
4	whole-wheat pita breads (6 inches in diameter)
	lettuce leaves
1	medium tomato, seeded and chopped ($\frac{3}{4}$ cup)
$\frac{1}{2}$	medium cucumber, sliced and cut into fourths
$\frac{1}{2}$	cup Creamy Cucumber Dressing *(p. 138)* *or* purchased creamy cucumber dressing

1. Place beans, water, parsley, walnuts, onion, and garlic in food processor or blender. Cover and process until smooth.
2. Cut each pita bread in half to form two pockets; line with lettuce leaves. Spoon sandwich filling into each pita half. Add tomato, cucumber, and dressing. Serve.

Serves 4
Prep. time: 10 minutes

MENU PLANNING TIPS
This is a great lunch box idea. Put the dressing in a small sealed container and drizzle over the sandwich filling just before eating.

MEXICAN CHILI BURGERS

1½	cups water
1	cup seven-grain cereal
10	ounces soft tofu, blended, *or* ½ cup egg whites *or* egg substitute
1-2	teaspoons McKay's Chicken-Style Seasoning *or* Chicken-like Seasoning *(p. 135)*
¼	cup fresh cilantro, minced
2-3	teaspoons canned green chilies, chopped
1½	teaspoons dried oregano
1½	teaspoons cumin
1	teaspoon chili powder
2	teaspoons garlic powder
1	cup onions, chopped fine
½	cup carrots, shredded
2	cups cooked brown rice
½-1	cup cracker crumbs
1	cup plum tomatoes, seeded and chopped

1. In a small microwaveable bowl, combine 1½ cups of water with the seven-grain cereal, cover, and cook on high for 5 minutes. Grains should be softened. Let sit to cool while preparing the remaining ingredients.
2. In blender container, blend the soft tofu to the consistency of soft cottage cheese. If tofu is too thick, add a small amount of water. If using the egg whites, slightly beat them.
3. In large mixing bowl, pour blended tofu or beaten eggs and add McKay's Chicken-Style Seasoning or Chicken-like Seasoning, cilantro, green chilies, oregano, cumin, chili powder, and garlic powder. Mix well. Add the onions, carrots, rice, cracker crumbs, tomatoes, and softened grain mixture. Mix well. If mixture is too thin to form burgers, add additional cracker crumbs. If mixture is too crumbly, add a few tablespoons of water to hold mixture together.
4. Shape into patties that are 4 inches in diameter and ½ inch in thickness.
5. Spray nonstick skillet with nonstick cooking spray and place over medium heat. Add the patties and sauté for about 5 minutes per side, or until golden brown.

OVEN-BAKED MEXI-FRIES

1½	pounds *or* seven medium baking potatoes, peeled and cut into thin strips
1	tablespoon canola *or* light olive oil
2	teaspoons chili powder
½	teaspoon salt (optional)
½	teaspoon dried oregano
¼	teaspoon garlic powder
¼	teaspoon ground cumin

1. Preheat oven to 450°F.
2. Combine all ingredients in a bowl; toss well. Arrange potatoes in a single layer on a baking sheet. Bake for 15 to 20 minutes, or until golden brown.

Makes 12 four-inch burgers,
½ inch thick
Prep. time: 10 minutes
Cooking time: 15-20 minutes

MENU PLANNING TIPS

Serve this great-tasting Mexican Chili Burger on whole-wheat burger buns spread with Tofu Sour Cream *(p. 136)* or fat-free sour cream. Add chopped green leaf lettuce. Guacamole and salsa add the final touch. Accompany burgers with the Oven-baked Mexi-Fries (recipe following) to add a unique taste. These burgers taste great in an open-faced sandwich. Just leave off the top half.

Serves 4
Prep. time: 10 minutes
Baking time: 15-20 minutes

Lunch Salads

SALADS

Waldorf Potato Salad

Waldorf Potato Salad Dressing

Summer Harvest Chicken-
Potato Salad

Soy Ranch Dressing

Caesar Salad

Freshly Made Croutons

Italian Spice Blend

Caesar Salad Dressing

Haystacks

Garden Greek Salad

Greek Salad Dressing

WALDORF POTATO SALAD

8	thin-skinned potatoes, peeled and chopped in large pieces
1	cup Waldorf Potato Salad Dressing (recipe following)
4	Golden Delicious apples, cored, peeled, and chopped
1	cup celery, chopped
½	cup red grapes, cut in half
¼-½	cup walnuts (optional)

1. Prepare and cook potatoes.
2. Prepare Waldorf Potato Salad Dressing.
3. In mixing bowl, combine potatoes, apples, celery, grapes, walnuts (optional); mix well.
4. Toss dressing over potato-apple mixture, evenly coating all ingredients with dressing.
5. Chill until serving time.

WALDORF POTATO SALAD DRESSING

1	cup water
½	cup Soyagen (soy milk powder)
1	pinch salt
2	tablespoons sugar *or* honey
2-3	tablespoons Hidden Valley Ranch dressing mix, to taste
½	cup light olive oil *or* canola oil
	juice of two large limes

In blender, place water, Soyagen,* salt, honey or sugar, and ranch dressing mix and process until smooth. While blending, slowly pour oil into mixture. Mixture will thicken. Pour mixture out into container. Stir in fresh lime juice.

If you do not have access to Soyagen, a soy milk powder, do not use any other soy or tofu milk powder; it will not thicken. It is best to replace the water and Soyagen with 10 ounces tofu, blended with enough water to thin to white-sauce consistency.

Serves 12
Prep. time: 10 minutes
Cooking time: 20 minutes

MENU PLANNING TIPS
This makes a great side dish to any meal. The combination of apples and potatoes may sound different, but you'll be pleasantly surprised at the great flavor when you try it.

Makes 2 cups

SUMMER HARVEST CHICKEN-POTATO SALAD

Serves 4-6
Prep. time: 15 minutes
Cooking time: 20 minutes

8	small red potatoes with skins, halved
2	cups green beans, fresh *or* frozen, trimmed and cut into 1-inch pieces
1	12.5-ounce can low-fat Worthington FriChik, each piece cut into 3 strips, then halved
2	cups celery, thinly sliced
½	sweet red pepper, sliced and chopped
1	cup Soy Ranch Dressing (recipe following)
	or
1	cup Yogurt Ranch Dressing:
	½ cup nonfat plain yogurt
	⅓ cup purchased fat-free ranch salad dressing
	torn salad greens for bed of lettuce

MENU PLANNING TIPS
Make a meal with this Summer Harvest Chicken-Potato Salad. Accompany it with some whole-grain rolls or bread.

1. In large saucepan, add small amount of water to the potatoes and steam until potatoes are just tender. Remove potatoes from pan with a slotted spoon, and cool. Add green beans to pan with potato water and cook an additional 5 to 7 minutes, or until green beans are just tender. Drain; rinse briefly with cold water to stop additional cooking. Place in large serving bowl.
2. Add FriChik, celery, and red pepper.
3. If using Soy Ranch Dressing, see the recipe following. If using the Yogurt Ranch Dressing, combine ingredients in a small bowl and blend well.
4. Pour dressing of choice over salad; toss gently. Serve immediately on plates lined with salad greens, or refrigerate until serving time.

SOY RANCH DRESSING

Makes 2 cups

1	cup water
⅔	cup Soyagen (soy milk powder)
1	pinch salt
1	tablespoon sugar *or* honey
4	tablespoons Hidden Valley Ranch dressing mix
¼	teaspoon garlic powder
¼	teaspoon onion powder
½	cup light olive oil *or* canola oil
	juice of two large limes *or* one lemon

1. In blender, place water, Soyagen,* salt, honey or sugar, ranch dressing mix, garlic powder, and onion powder and process until smooth. While blending, slowly pour oil into mixture. Mixture will thicken. Pour mixture into a container.
2. Stir in fresh lime or lemon juice. Dressing should thicken more with the addition of lime or lemon juice. Chill in sealed container until serving.

*If you do not have access to Soyagen, a soy milk powder, do not use any other soy or tofu milk powder; it will not thicken. It is best to replace the water and Soyagen with ⅔ cup tofu, blended with enough water to thin to white-sauce consistency.

Serves 12
Prep. time: 10 minutes
Cooking time: 5 minutes

CAESAR SALAD

	1	12.5-ounce can Worthington FriChik (optional), drained, cut into strips
or	1	10-ounce package firm tofu, cut into 1-inch cubes
	½	teaspoon Italian Spice Blend (recipe following)
	¼	teaspoon garlic powder
	¼	teaspoon McKay's Chicken-Style Seasoning *or* Chicken-like Seasoning *(p. 135)*
	6	cups Romaine lettuce, torn into bite-size pieces
	3	cups green leaf lettuce *or* spinach leaves, torn into bite-size pieces
	1	carrot, peeled and grated
	2	cups Freshly Made Croutons (recipe following)
		Caesar Salad Dressing *(p. 67)*
		freshly-grated Parmesan cheese or Cheeseless "Parmesan" Cheese *(p. 141)*

1. Drain FriChik or tofu; cut FriChik into strips or tofu into cubes. In bowl, combine FriChik or tofu, Italian Spice Blend, garlic powder, and McKay's Chicken-Style Seasoning or Chicken-like Seasoning and toss well. Coat nonstick skillet with non-stick cooking spray; place over medium-high heat until hot. Add seasoned FriChik or tofu; cook 4 minutes on each side, or until browned. Remove from skillet; let cool.

2. Combine lettuce, carrots, 1½ cups of the croutons, and seasoned FriChik or tofu in a large bowl; toss well. Drizzle dressing over Caesar salad mixture; toss well to coat evenly.

3. Place 2 cups of salad on each of four salad plates. Top with remaining ½ cup croutons. Freshly grated Parmesan cheese or Cheeseless "Parmesan" Cheese can be lightly sprinkled over salad, if desired.

FRESHLY MADE CROUTONS

2	cups (about 4 slices) whole-wheat bread, cut into 1-inch cubes
	olive oil-flavored nonstick cooking spray
1	teaspoon Italian Spice Blend (recipe following)
¼	teaspoon garlic powder
	dash salt (optional)

1. Preheat oven to 350°F.

2. Arrange bread cubes in a single layer on baking sheet. Lightly coat bread cubes with cooking spray and sprinkle with Italian Spice Blend (recipe following), garlic powder, and salt to taste. Toss well. Rearrange seasoned bread cubes in single layer. Bake at 350°F for 15 minutes, or until lightly browned; set aside.

ITALIAN SPICE BLEND

2	tablespoons fresh oregano, chopped, *or* 2 teaspoons dried oregano
1	tablespoon fresh basil, chopped, *or* 1 teaspoon dried basil
1	tablespoon fresh mint, *or* 1 teaspoon dried mint
½	teaspoon rubbed sage
1	teaspoon granulated garlic
½	teaspoon onion powder

Place all ingredients in a clean spice or coffee grinder; process until finely ground. Store in an airtight container.

CAESAR SALAD DRESSING

1	recipe tofu *or* yogurt cheese *(option recipes below)*
2-3	tablespoons water
1	teaspoon dry mustard
1½	teaspoons fresh lemon juice (replacement for balsamic vinegar)
1-2	garlic cloves, minced (depending on your love of garlic)

Combine tofu or yogurt option with water, dry mustard, lemon juice, and garlic in blender or food processor; process well. Set dressing aside. Dressing should be thin. If needed, add additional water to thin the sauce. (Try adding ½ to 1 teaspoon Italian Spice Blend *[p. 66]* to this dressing for variety.)

TOFU OPTION:

1	cup soft tofu
2	tablespoons vegetable oil
1	tablespoon lemon juice
1½	teaspoons honey
½	teaspoon salt

Combine ingredients and blend until smooth.

YOGURT CHEESE OPTION:

8	ounces plain nonfat yogurt

Place colander in a medium bowl. Line colander with four layers of cheesecloth, allowing cheesecloth to extend over outside of edges. Spoon yogurt into colander. Cover loosely with plastic wrap; refrigerate 12 hours. Discard liquid.

Prep. time:
5 minutes/tofu option
Overnight /yogurt option

HAYSTACKS

½	cup cooked pinto beans *or* small red beans
2	tablespoons green chilies
¼	teaspoon garlic powder
¼	teaspoon cumin
¼	teaspoon chili powder (more or less, depending on how spicy you like your beans)
1	cup low-fat tortilla chips
1	cup head lettuce, shredded
1	small Roma tomato, chopped
¼	cup carrots, grated
1	tablespoon green onions, sliced (optional)
1	tablespoon black olives, sliced (optional)
2	tablespoons Guacamole *(p. 140)*
2	tablespoons low-fat sour cream *or* Tofu Sour Cream *(p. 136)*
2	tablespoons Thick and Chunky Salsa *(p. 139)*

1. In small saucepan, combine beans, green chilies, garlic powder, cumin, and chili powder and cook over medium heat until heated thoroughly.

2. Place chips on serving plate. Spoon the warm chili bean mixture over the chips. Top the bean mixture with lettuce, tomato, carrots, guacamole, sour cream, and salsa. Serve immediately.

Serves 1
Prep time: 10 minutes
Cooking time: 10 minutes

MENU PLANNING TIPS
Haystacks are a regular weekly menu item for many vegetarians. You can make them many ways. Changing the beans, chips, and toppings totally changes the taste. The goal is to keep the combination tasty and moist. The salsa, guacamole, and sour cream add the final touch.

GARDEN GREEK SALAD

Serves 6
Prep. time: 10 minutes
Cooking time: 10 minutes

- 1   cup pasta bows
- 1/4   cup Greek Salad Dressing (recipe following)
- 4   cups Romaine lettuce, torn into bite-size pieces
- 1/2   cup carrots, grated
- 1/2   green pepper, thinly sliced, **and/or** sweet red pepper
- 1/4   cup artichoke hearts, not marinated
- 1/4   cup black olives, sliced
- 1   teaspoon feta cheese (optional)

1. Cook pasta until just tender and drain.
2. Prepare the Greek Salad Dressing and chill until serving time.
3. Prepare and toss together lettuce, carrots, green peppers, artichoke hearts, and black olives. Add cooked pasta and toss. Toss dressing over the entire vegetable/pasta mixture. Place in serving bowl and garnish with feta cheese, if desired.

MENU PLANNING TIPS

This is one of my favorite main dish salads. Serve this with garlic bread and enjoy the feast. The pasta added to the lettuce is an interesting twist. It gives this salad a hearty feel, and you'll never miss the feta cheese traditionally served with Greek salad, if you opt not to use cheese.

GREEK SALAD DRESSING

Makes 1/2 cup

- 1/3   cup fresh lemon juice
- 4   tablespoons light olive oil
- 1/2   teaspoon honey **or** pinch sugar
- 2   tablespoons green onion, sliced thin (optional)
- 1   tablespoon fresh oregano **or** 1 teaspoon dried oregano
- 1/4   teaspoon salt (optional)
- 2   garlic cloves, minced

1. Mix all dressing ingredients in a container that can be shaken. Shake well until oil and lemon juice have a creamy appearance. Chill until serving. Shake before serving each time.

Lunch Soups

SOUPS

Vegetable Split-Pea Soup

Chilled Minted Pea Soup

Chilled Chunky Gazpacho

Creamy Broccoli-Rice Soup

Vegetable Chili

Creamy Garlic Potato Soup

Italian Vegetable Soup

VEGETABLE SPLIT-PEA SOUP

2	quarts water
2	cups dried green split peas
1	stalk celery, coarsely chopped
1	large carrot, chopped
1	small onion, chopped
1/4	teaspoon ground thyme
1	whole bay leaf
	salt to taste
1	package golden George Washington Broth *or* 1 teaspoon McKay's Chicken-Style Seasoning

1. Rinse peas thoroughly in fine strainer under cold water, picking out debris and any blemished peas. Prepare vegetables as directed.
2. In large pan, combine all the above prepared ingredients and bring to a boil for 20 minutes. Cover and let simmer additional 30 minutes. Remove bay leaf before serving.

Serves 8-12
Prep. time: 10 minutes
Cooking time: 1 hour

MENU PLANNING TIPS
This wonderful split-pea soup meal is completed by serving with a tossed green salad and whole-grain rolls. The soup can be slow cooked in a Crock-Pot, ready for dinner when you get home.

CHILLED MINTED PEA SOUP

1	cup dried green split peas
1	carrot, peeled and sliced
1/2	cup onion, chopped
1/2	cup celery, chopped
2	tablespoons light olive oil
4	cups water
4	teaspoons McKay's Chicken-Style Seasoning *or* Chicken-like Seasoning *(p. 135)*
2	tablespoons fresh mint leaves, chopped, *or* 2 teaspoons dried mint leaves
1	teaspoon sugar or honey
	salt to taste (optional)
1	cup Tofu Sour Cream *(p. 136) or* nonfat sour cream

1. Rinse peas thoroughly in fine strainer under cold running water, picking out debris and any blemished peas. Set aside.
2. Prepare carrot, onions, and celery.
3. In medium saucepan over medium heat, add oil, carrot, onions, and celery. Cook 5 minutes, or until vegetables are tender, stirring occasionally.
4. Stir in water and McKay's Chicken-Style Seasoning or Chicken-like Seasoning, peas, and 1 tablespoon fresh mint or 1 teaspoon dried mint. Bring to a boil over medium-high heat. Reduce to low; simmer, covered, 1 hour, or until peas are very tender.
5. Place soup in food processor. Add remaining mint, sugar or honey, and salt to taste. Process until smooth, scraping side of bowl occasionally.
6. Place soup in medium bowl; stir in Tofu Sour Cream or nonfat sour cream. Cover tightly with plastic wrap. Refrigerate 3 to 4 hours until well chilled. Garnish with nonfat sour cream or Tofu Sour Cream and fresh mint leaves, if desired.

Serves 4-6
Prep. time: 20 minutes
Cooking time: 45 minutes

MENU PLANNING TIPS
This soup makes a great appetizer or chilled soup for dinner on a hot summer day.

CHILLED CHUNKY GAZPACHO

Serves 8
Prep. time: 15 minutes

MENU PLANNING TIPS
Cool gazpacho is now an American classic. It makes a great summer soup served with toasted crackers or garlic bread to top off the light meal.

6	cups tomatoes, coarsely chopped *(about 3 pounds)*
1	32-ounce bottle low-sodium tomato juice
2	cups cucumber, peeled and chopped *(about 2 medium)*
1½	cups green bell pepper, chopped
1½	cups Vidalia *or* sweet onion, finely chopped
1	cup celery, chopped
1	tablespoon olive oil
3	tablespoons lemon juice
½	teaspoon salt
½	teaspoon hot sauce
3	garlic cloves, minced

Combine all ingredients in a large bowl; stir well. Cover and chill. Serving size is 1½ cups.

CREAMY BROCCOLI-RICE SOUP

Serves 4
Prep. time: 10 minutes
Cooking time: 20 minutes

MENU PLANNING TIPS
The secret to making this creamy soup without cream is the puréeing of the vegetable mixture in a blender or food processor. Add a tossed salad or raw vegetable sticks and whole grain bread for a light, low-fat meal.

⅓	cup water
3	cups broccoli florets
½	cup chopped onion
3½	cups water
4	teaspoons McKay's Chicken-Style Seasoning *or* Chicken-like Seasoning *(p. 135)*
½	cup uncooked brown or regular white rice
1	cup tofu *or* soy *or* nonfat milk
1	teaspoon fresh oregano leaves *or* ¼ teaspoon dried oregano leaves
½	teaspoon salt (optional)

1. Heat ⅓ cup of water to boiling in 3-quart saucepan over medium heat. Add broccoli and onion. Boil uncovered 6 to 8 minutes, or until almost tender; drain and set aside.

2. Heat 3½ cups water, McKay's Chicken-Style Seasoning or Chicken-like Seasoning, and rice to boiling; reduce heat. Cover and simmer 18 to 20 minutes, or until rice is tender. Place half the broccoli mixture and half the rice mixture in food processor or blender. Cover and process until smooth; return to saucepan. Repeat with remaining broccoli and rice mixtures; return to saucepan. Stir in remaining ingredients; heat through. Serve.

VEGETABLE CHILI

2	medium potatoes, cubed (2 cups)
1	medium onion, chopped (¹/₂ cup)
1	small yellow, red, *or* green bell pepper, chopped (¹/₂ cup)
1	tablespoon chili powder
1	teaspoon ground cumin
1	28-ounce can whole tomatoes, undrained
1	15-ounce can garbanzo beans, rinsed and drained
1	15-ounce can black beans, rinsed and drained
1	8-ounce can tomato purée
¹/₂	teaspoon garlic powder
1	teaspoon lemon juice
¹/₂	teaspoon sugar *or* honey
1	medium zucchini, cubed (1 cup)

Garnish with the following:

nonfat sour cream or Tofu Sour Cream *(p. 136)*

chopped fresh cilantro *or* parsley, if desired

1. In saucepan, combine all ingredients, except zucchini, sour cream, and cilantro or parsley. Heat to boiling, breaking up tomatoes and stirring occasionally. Reduce heat. Cover and simmer 13 minutes.
2. Stir in zucchini. Cover and simmer 5 to 7 minutes, or until zucchini is tender. Serve with garnishes.

Serves 8
Prep. time: 10 minutes
Cooking time: 15-20 minutes

MENU PLANNING TIPS
This vegetable chili can be made with any combination of beans. Add more or less chili powder, depending on preferred taste. Serve this chili with corn bread for a Mexican fiesta.

CREAMY GARLIC POTATO SOUP

1	tablespoon light olive oil
¹/₂	cup onion, chopped
4	garlic cloves, minced *or* sliced thin
4	cups water
4	teaspoons vegetable broth *or* McKay's Chicken-Style Seasoning *or* Chicken-like Seasoning *(p. 135)*
3	cups potatoes, diced
1	cup fat-free sour cream *or* Tofu Sour Cream *(p. 136)*
2	tablespoons fresh dill, chopped, *or* 2 teaspoons dried dill
	salt to taste (optional)

1. In large pot, heat oil over medium-high heat. Add onion and sauté until translucent; add garlic to onions and sauté an additional 2 to 3 minutes.
2. Add water and broth or seasoning mix and bring to boil. Add potatoes and return to boil. Reduce heat to medium and boil gently 10 minutes, or until potatoes are tender.
3. Working with half of mixture at a time, transfer to food processor or blender. Process until puréed. Return to pot. Stir in remaining ingredients. Stir over low heat until heated through. Serve warm. Garnish with fresh dill and/or green onion slices.

Serves 6
Prep. time: 10 minutes
Cooking time: 15 minutes

MENU PLANNING TIPS
This creamy potato soup features sautéed garlic and fresh dill, which add intense flavor. Serve this soup with a tossed green salad and whole-grain bread or toast.

ITALIAN VEGETABLE SOUP

ITALIAN VEGETABLE SOUP

Serves 8
Prep. time: 10 minutes
Cooking time: 30 minutes

4	cups water
4	teaspoons vegetable broth *or* McKay's Chicken-Style Seasoning *or* Chicken-like Seasoning *(p. 135)*
2	large tomatoes, chopped and seeded (1 cup)
2	medium carrots, sliced (1 cup)
1	medium stalk celery, sliced ($\frac{1}{2}$ cup)
1	medium onion, chopped ($\frac{1}{2}$ cup)
2	garlic cloves, minced
1	tablespoon fresh parsley, chopped
$1\frac{1}{2}$	teaspoons fresh basil, chopped, *or* $\frac{1}{2}$ teaspoon dried basil
$\frac{1}{4}$	teaspoon salt
1	whole bay leaf
$\frac{1}{2}$	cup uncooked macaroni
1	15-ounce can red *or* white kidney beans, rinsed and drained
$\frac{1}{4}$	cup green beans, cut
2	small zucchini, cut into 1-inch slices (2 cups)

1. In large saucepan, heat water, vegetable broth, tomatoes, carrots, celery, onion, garlic, parsley, basil, salt, and bay leaf to boiling. Reduce heat. Cover and simmer 15 minutes.

2. Stir in macaroni, beans, green beans, and zucchini. Heat to boiling. reduce heat. Cover and simmer 10 to 15 minutes, or until macaroni and vegetables are tender. Remove bay leaf. Serve warm.

MENU PLANNING TIPS

You can use any pasta and any beans that you like for this recipe. Serve with hard rolls or garlic bread on the side.

Main Dish Dinner

PASTA

Chili Macaroni

Pasta With Basil and Tomatoes

Vermicelli With Chunky
Vegetable Sauce

Sun-dried Tomato-Red Pepper
Pesto With Pasta

Linguine With Fresh
Tomato Sauce

Fresh Basil Pesto With Pasta

Asparagus "Alfredo" Pasta Bows

Angel Hair Vegetable Toss

Pasta Tossed With Seasoned Olive
Oil and Fresh Basil

Fettuccine Primavera "Alfredo"

Vegetable Lasagna

CHILI MACARONI

1	cup Loma Linda Redi-Burger *or* cubed firm tofu (optional)
1	medium onion, chopped
1	green pepper, chopped
1	14½-ounce can diced tomatoes
½	cup tomato paste
1	cup water
1	4-ounce can diced green chili peppers, drained
2	teaspoons chili powder
½	teaspoon garlic powder
1	teaspoon oregano
1	teaspoon sugar *or* honey
1	tablespoon lemon juice
	salt to taste (optional)
1	15-ounce can kidney beans
1	cup uncooked macaroni
1	cup loose-pack frozen cut green beans, 1 inch long

1. In large, nonstick skillet over medium heat, cook the burger (if using), onion, and green pepper.
2. Stir in undrained canned diced tomatoes, tomato paste, water, green chili peppers, chili powder, garlic powder, oregano, sugar or honey, lemon juice, salt, and kidney beans. Bring to a boil.
3. Stir in uncooked macaroni and green beans. Return to boiling; reduce heat. Simmer, covered, about 15 minutes, or until macaroni and green beans are tender. Serve in bowls.

Serves 8-10
Prep. time: 15 minutes
Cooking time: 15 minutes

MENU PLANNING TIPS
Serve this speedy skillet meal with corn bread on the side. Use Redi-Burger, a vegetarian burger, tofu, or delete burger.

PASTA WITH BASIL AND TOMATOES

8	ounces dried penne pasta
2	tablespoons olive oil
¼	cup fresh Parmesan cheese, finely grated *or* Cheeseless "Parmesan" Cheese *(p. 141)* (optional)
½	cup green onion, chopped
8	Roma tomatoes, cored, seeded, and chopped
1½	cups lightly packed, chopped fresh basil leaves, plus some sprigs

1. Bring water for pasta to a boil over high heat. Stir in pasta and cook until just tender, about 10 minutes. Drain well; pour into a wide serving bowl. Add 1 tablespoon olive oil and 2 tablespoons Parmesan cheese (optional); mix well and keep warm.
2. In a 10- to 12-inch nonstick skillet over medium-high heat, stir onions in remaining oil until limp, about 5 minutes. Add tomatoes and stir just until tomatoes are hot, about 2 minutes; stir in chopped basil.
3. Pour tomato mixture over hot cooked pasta. Garnish with basil sprigs and optional Parmesan cheese.

Serves 5
Prep. time: 10 minutes
Cooking time: 20 minutes

VERMICELLI WITH CHUNKY VEGETABLE SAUCE

Serves 6
Prep. time: 10 minutes
Cooking time: 10 minutes

MENU PLANNING TIPS

This Chunky Vegetable Sauce is the family favorite at our house. Your whole meal is in this pasta dish. Simply add garlic bread, and you're set. Fresh basil and oregano add the flavoring for this wonderful, fresh garden sauce.

³/₄	pound dried vermicelli pasta
1	sweet red pepper, chopped
1	medium onion, chopped
2	stalks celery, chopped
2	small zucchini, sliced
3-4	cloves garlic
4	cups canned diced tomatoes
1	6-ounce can tomato paste
	salt to taste (optional)
1	tablespoon sugar *or* honey
1	tablespoon lemon juice
¹/₄	cup fresh basil leaves *or* 2 tablespoons dried basil
2	tablespoons fresh oregano leaves *or* 2 teaspoons dried oregano

1. Bring water for pasta to a boil over high heat; stir in pasta and cook until just tender, about 5 to 7 minutes. Drain well; pour into a wide serving bowl.

2. In nonstick skillet over medium-high heat, stir red peppers, onion, and celery until tender, about 5 minutes. Add zucchini and garlic; cook until zucchini is tender. Add tomatoes, tomato paste, salt, sugar or honey, and lemon juice. Stir until tomato mixture comes to a boil, about 5 minutes. Add basil and oregano and cook an additional minute.

3. Serve Chunky Vegetable Sauce over pasta.

SUN-DRIED TOMATO-RED PEPPER PESTO WITH PASTA

Serves 4
Prep. time: 10 minutes
Cooking time: 10 minutes

MENU PLANNING TIPS

This is an easy-to-prepare dish that can be made in 20 minutes. Try tossing in whole pine nuts with pasta for texture. Serve with steamed broccoli, tossed green salad, and garlic bread.

8	ounces dried penne pasta *or* pasta of choice
12	sun-dried tomato halves
¹/₄	cup fresh basil leaves
2	plum tomatoes, coarsely chopped
2-3	garlic cloves
1-2	roasted red peppers, chopped
¹/₄-¹/₂	cup pine nuts
	salt to taste (optional)
¹/₂	teaspoon onion powder
¹/₂	teaspoon McKay's Chicken-Style Seasoning or Chicken-like Seasoning *(p. 135)*
¹/₈	cup olive oil

1. Bring water for pasta to a boil over high heat; stir in pasta and cook just until tender, about 15 minutes. Drain well.

2. Rehydrate sun-dried tomato halves by soaking in boiling water for 2 minutes.

3. In blender or food processor, place basil leaves and process until finely chopped, scraping sides as needed. Add rehydrated sun-dried tomatoes, plum tomatoes, garlic cloves, roasted red peppers, pine nuts, salt, onion powder, and McKay's Chicken-Style Seasoning or Chicken-like Seasoning. While machine is running, pour in olive oil. Thin with 2 to 4 tablespoons of hot water, if needed, to toss with pasta.

4. Toss pesto with hot pasta and serve.

LINGUINE WITH FRESH TOMATO SAUCE

³/₄	pound fresh *or* dried linguine
1	teaspoon olive oil
1	small onion, chopped
2	yellow *or* red bell peppers, chopped
4	cloves garlic, minced
3	pounds Roma tomatoes, cored and coarsely chopped
1	cup lightly packed fresh basil leaves, slivered
	or
1	cup lightly packed fresh spinach leaves, slivered, with 1 tablespoon dried basil
1	tablespoon lemon juice
1	tablespoon sugar *or* honey to taste (optional)
	Parmesan cheese *or* Cheeseless "Parmesan" Cheese *(p. 141)* (optional)
	salt to taste

1. Bring water for pasta to a boil over high heat. Add pasta and cook, uncovered, just until tender, about 8 minutes. Drain well. To serve hot, pour into a wide bowl. To serve cold, immerse pasta in cool water until cold, then drain well and pour into a wide bowl.

2. In a 3- to 4-quart pan over medium heat, add 1 teaspoon olive oil, onion, and two thirds of the peppers. Cook until vegetables are just tender; add the garlic, and cook an additional 2 minutes. Add two thirds of the tomatoes, ½ cup of the slivered basil, lemon juice, and sweetener of choice. Stir often until tomatoes begin to fall apart, about 10 minutes. Use hot, or let cool to room temperature; cover when cool and let stand, up to 6 hours. Stir into hot or cold cooked tomato mixture the remaining one third of the tomatoes, one third of the peppers, and ½ cup of slivered fresh basil or spinach-dried basil mixture.

3. Spoon hot sauce onto hot pasta, or cool sauce onto cool pasta; mix. Garnish with fresh basil sprigs. Add Parmesan cheese or Cheeseless "Parmesan" Cheese and/or salt to taste, if desired; serve.

Serves 6
Prep. time: 10 minutes
Cooking time: 15 minutes

MENU PLANNING TIPS
This light and refreshing pasta dish can be served hot or cold. Serve with a fresh tossed green salad and whole-grain bread.

FRESH BASIL PESTO WITH PASTA

³⁄₄	pound pasta of choice
¹⁄₂	cup fresh basil leaves *or* ¹⁄₂ cup fresh spinach leaves and ¹⁄₂-1 tablespoon dried basil
¹⁄₃	cup pine nuts, plus 3 tablespoons
2	cloves garlic
¹⁄₄	cup olive oil
¹⁄₂	teaspoon McKay's Chicken-Style Seasoning *or* Chicken-like Seasoning *(p. 135)*
2	tablespoons hot water

1. Bring a large pot of water to a boil. Cook pasta according to package directions while preparing the pesto.

2. Place fresh basil in food processor or blender and process until finely chopped, scraping sides as needed. Add pine nuts and garlic, and process until finely chopped. With machine running, pour in olive oil in a thin stream. Add McKay's Chicken-Style Seasoning or Chicken-like Seasoning and process briefly to combine. Thin with 2 tablespoons hot water.

3. Toss pesto with hot pasta (cooked and drained) and serve.

Serves 4
Prep. time: 10 minutes
Cooking time: 10 minutes

MENU PLANNING TIPS
This light-tasting, basil-flavored pasta is very satisfying. Try adding warm cannellini (white kidney) beans tossed in with the pesto and pasta. Serve with tossed green salad and whole-grain bread. Garnish with whole pine nuts.

ASPARAGUS "ALFREDO" PASTA BOWS

8	ounces fettuccine pasta
1	pound fresh asparagus *or* broccoli
1	tablespoon olive oil
1	cup "Alfredo" sauce *(see Fettuccine Primavera "Alfredo" recipe, p. 83)*

1. Bring water for pasta to a boil over high heat. Add pasta; cook until tender, 8 to 10 minutes. Drain well; pour into a wide serving bowl.

2. Wash asparagus and scrape off scales, using a vegetable peeler. Break off woody bases where spears snap easily; discard bases. Slice asparagus diagonally into 1-inch pieces. Cook in a small amount of boiling water for 3 to 5 minutes, or till crisp-tender. Drain well.

3. Add "Alfredo" sauce and asparagus pieces to pasta and toss well, coating evenly. Serve immediately. Add freshly grated Parmesan cheese, if desired.

Serves 6
Prep. time: 5 minutes
Cooking time: 10 minutes

MENU PLANNING TIPS
This easy-to-prepare "Alfredo" dish can be made with asparagus or broccoli. The pasta bows are tossed with the garlic-flavored, cholesterol-free "Alfredo" sauce. This is so easy to prepare, and, served with a tossed green salad, it makes a very quick-to-prepare dinner.

ANGEL HAIR VEGETABLE TOSS

Serves 4
Prep. time: 15 minutes
Cooking time: 20 minutes

MENU PLANNING TIPS

This pasta dish is very light tasting and is tossed with lots of delicious vegetables. The chili flakes add a zesty flavor but are optional because they can be irritating to some people. Serve this full-meal dish with seasoned garlic toast and enjoy.

³⁄₄	pound broccoli florets
1	pound carrots, thinly sliced
³⁄₄	pound fresh *or* dried angel hair pasta
2	cups spinach leaves, whole or sliced
1	cup zucchini, sliced
1	cup mushrooms, sliced
1	cup green onions, sliced
2	garlic cloves, minced
2	cups vegetable *or* vegetarian chicken broth (2 cups hot water mixed with 2 teaspoons vegetable broth mix *or* McKay's Chicken-Style Seasoning *or* Chicken-like Seasoning *(p. 135)*
³⁄₄-1	cup dried tomatoes (not packed in oil), chopped fine
¹⁄₄	teaspoon hot chili flakes (optional)
3	tablespoons prepared capers, drained

1. Bring water for pasta to a boil over high heat. To the boiling water, add broccoli and cook until broccoli turns bright green and is slightly tender when pierced, about 1 minute. Remove broccoli from boiling water with a slotted spoon and set aside until step 4.

2. Add carrots to boiling water. Cook until carrots are tender when pierced, about 6 minutes. Without removing carrots, add pasta and spinach leaves to boiling water. Cook until pasta is just tender, 2 to 3 minutes. Drain pasta and vegetables well; keep warm.

3. Meanwhile, in nonstick skillet, lightly brown zucchini, mushrooms, green onions, and garlic. Add broth, tomatoes, and chili flakes. Bring mixture to a boil over high heat; reduce heat to keep warm.

4. In large serving bowl, combine pasta-vegetable mixture and sautéed vegetable-broth mixture, broccoli, and capers. Transfer to a serving bowl or individual plates. Serve.

PASTA TOSSED WITH SEASONED OLIVE OIL AND FRESH BASIL

Serves 6
Prep. time: 15 minutes
Cooking time: 20 minutes

MENU PLANNING TIPS

The seasoned oil adds the flavor to this pasta toss. Experiment with different seasonings for your oil to change the flavor of this dish totally.

³⁄₄	pound dried linguine *or* fettuccine
1	onion, chopped
2	tablespoons hot chili olive oil *or* olive oil and ¹⁄₂ teaspoon hot chili flakes *(note: use any herb- or garlic-seasoned olive oil you prefer)*
2-4	cloves garlic, minced (depending on preference)
2	pounds ripe tomatoes, rinsed, cored, and coarsely chopped
2	cups firmly packed fresh basil leaves, slivered
	or
2	cups firmly packed fresh spinach leaves, slivered, and 1-2 tablespoons dried basil
	salt to taste optional
	Parmesan cheese *or* Cheeseless "Parmesan" Cheese *(p. 141)* (optional)

1. Bring water for pasta to a boil over high heat. Add pasta; cook until tender, 8 to 10 minutes. Drain well; pour into a wide serving bowl.

2. In a 10- to 12-inch frying pan over medium-high heat, combine onion and oil; stir often until onion is golden, about 8 to 10 minutes. Add garlic and cook an additional 2 minutes.

3. Add tomatoes. (If less-juicy sauce is desired, cut tomatoes in half crosswise and squeeze out and discard seeds before chopping.) Turn heat to high and stir until tomatoes are hot, 2 to 3 minutes. Remove from heat, stir in slivered basil and salt, and pour over pasta. Sprinkle with fresh grated Parmesan to taste, if desired.

FETTUCCINE PRIMAVERA "ALFREDO"

16	ounces fettuccine pasta
1-2	tablespoons olive oil
	salt (optional)
½-1	onion, chopped small
1	red pepper, chopped
4	garlic cloves, minced
4	carrots, thinly sliced
2	small zucchini, sliced
3	cups broccoli, cut in bite-size pieces
	Parmesan cheese *or* Cheeseless "Parmesan" Cheese *(p. 141)* (optional)

"ALFREDO" SAUCE:

10	ounces tofu, soft
2	tablespoons olive oil
1½	tablespoons lemon juice
1	tablespoon honey
½	teaspoon salt
¼	cup tofu *or* soy *or* nonfat milk
¼	teaspoon garlic, granulated
¼	teaspoon onion powder
¼	teaspoon McKay's Chicken-Style Seasoning *or* Chicken-like Seasoning *(p. 135)* (optional)

1. In large pan, bring water to boil for pasta. Add pasta and cook until tender. Drain; toss pasta with 1 tablespoon olive oil and salt to taste (optional).

2. In nonstick skillet, add olive oil, onion, and red pepper; sauté until just tender. Add thinly sliced carrots, zucchini, and broccoli and cook until tender. Add garlic and sauté an additional 2 minutes.

3. In blender, combine all the "Alfredo" sauce ingredients and blend until smooth.

4. Toss the cooked vegetables into the warm pasta. Then add the "Alfredo" sauce and mix to coat pasta evenly with sauce. Serve immediately. Top with freshly grated Parmesan cheese, if desired.

Serves 6
Prep. time: 10 minutes
Cooking time: 10 minutes

MENU PLANNING TIPS

This delicious cholesterol-free fettuccine can be enjoyed even while trying to watch your weight or on a low-cholesterol diet. The sauce is made with tofu blended in. Don't let this stop you from trying this recipe! When the tofu is blended with other seasonings, it takes on the flavor of the seasonings and adds that thick, creamy consistency to the sauce. Try adding fresh herbs to the sauce for variety. Developing a healthy fettuccine Alfredo sauce was challenging, but this sauce won First Place with many. Add a fresh green salad, and you'll have another heart-healthy meal.

VEGETABLE LASAGNA

VEGETABLE LASAGNA

1   18-ounce box dried lasagna noodles

2   large carrots, sliced

2   cups broccoli florets in bite-size pieces

VEGETABLE TOMATO SAUCE:

1   tablespoon olive oil

2   stalks celery, sliced

1   large sweet red bell pepper, chopped

2   small zucchini, sliced

2   small yellow squash, sliced

4   green onions, sliced *or* chopped

4-6   garlic cloves, minced

4   tablespoons fresh basil leaves *or* 4 teaspoons dried basil

2   tablespoons fresh oregano *or* 2 teaspoons dried oregano

$\frac{1}{2}$ teaspoon salt (optional)

8   cups diced tomatoes

1   6-ounce can tomato paste

4   tablespoons lemon juice

4   tablespoons sugar *or* honey

HERBED TOFU CHEESE MIXTURE:

Dairy option: *(substitute ricotta cheese and 2 egg whites, slightly beaten, for tofu)*

1   pound tofu (2 cups), blended or mashed

2   tablespoons olive oil

1   tablespoon fresh lemon juice

1   tablespoon honey

2   teaspoons garlic powder

1   teaspoon dried basil

1. Bring water for lasagna noodles to a boil over high heat, and add pasta to boiling water. Cook until pasta is just tender, 8 to 10 minutes. Drain noodles and lay out flat to cool until ready to assemble lasagna.

2. In separate saucepan or covered casserole dish for microwaving, steam the carrots and broccoli until tender. Let cool until ready to assemble.

3. In nonstick skillet, add olive oil and heat. Add celery, red peppers, zucchini, and yellow squash; cook until tender. Add green onions, garlic, basil, oregano, and salt (optional). Continue to cook for 2 minutes. Add tomatoes, tomato paste, lemon juice, and sugar or honey. Add the steamed carrots and broccoli.

4. In blender, combine tofu *(or ricotta cheese and egg whites)*, olive oil, lemon juice, honey, garlic powder, and dried basil; blend until smooth.

5. To assemble: In 9" x 13" lasagna pan with 3-inch sides, sprayed with nonstick vegetable spray, add 3 cups of the vegetable tomato sauce. Top with a layer of lasagna noodles, slightly overlapping each piece. Top noodles with 3 cups of vegetable sauce mixture. Spoon onto the sauce half of the cheese mixture in three strips down the noodles. Repeat with second layer of noodles, the remaining vegetable tomato sauce (approximately 3 cups), and the remaining cheese mixture. Bake immediately, or refrigerate or freeze for baking later. Bake for 45 minutes at 350°F, or until top is lightly browned and casserole is bubbly. Drizzle small amount of reserved vegetable tomato sauce over individual portions just before serving.

Serves 12-15
Prep. time: 20 minutes
Cooking time: 45 minutes

MENU PLANNING TIPS

This lasagna is a real winner with everyone! Because this dish can be made ahead and frozen or refrigerated until later, it works great for entertaining. Although I make this recipe with both the dairy option and the tofu option, most people prefer the herbed tofu cheese mixture. The homemade vegetable tomato sauce is the key to the rich flavor, without the cheese or meat. Reserve a small amount of vegetable tomato sauce and drizzle across the top of each serving of lasagna.

Main Dish Dinner

RICE AND COUSCOUS

Brown Rice With Vegetables
and Tomato Pesto

Pesto Rice and Beans

Stir-fried Asian Vegetables

Spring Vegetable Curry

Teriyaki Stir-fry Over Rice

Grilled Vegetables Over Rice

Hearty Rice Skillet

Herbed "Chicken" Couscous
and Vegetables

Garden Vegetable Couscous

Couscous Alfresco

Curried "Chicken"
and Broccoli Couscous

Basil-roasted Vegetables
Over Couscous

Roasted-Pepper Bruschetta

Pesto Risotto

Basmati Rice Seasoned With
Dried Fruits and Nuts

Vegetable Medley Quiche
in Rice Crust

BROWN RICE WITH VEGETABLES AND TOMATO PESTO

Serves 10
Prep. time: 15 minutes
Cooking time: 30 minutes

1   tablespoon oil
1   medium onion, chopped
4   cloves garlic, minced
1½ cups uncooked brown rice
3   cups water
3   teaspoons McKay's Chicken-Style Seasoning *or* Chicken-like Seasoning *(p. 135)*
4   small carrots, sliced
1   cup green beans, cut in 1-inch lengths
2   cups broccoli florets
2   small zucchini *or* yellow summer squash, sliced
½   cup tomato pesto (recipe below)

1. Heat 1 tablespoon oil in 2-quart saucepan over medium-high heat. Add onion and garlic; cook and stir 3 minutes. Add rice; cook and stir 2 minutes. Gradually add water and McKay's Chicken-Style Seasoning or Chicken-like Seasoning. Bring to a boil over medium-high heat. Reduce heat to low; simmer, covered, 30 to 40 minutes, or until rice is tender and liquid is absorbed.

2. Heat 3 tablespoons water or olive oil in large, nonstick skillet over medium heat. Add carrots and beans; cook and stir 4 minutes. Add squash and broccoli; cook and stir 5 to 7 minutes until vegetables are crisp-tender. Combine rice mixture and vegetable mixture in large bowl. Gently toss with ½ cup tomato pesto.

TOMATO PESTO:

Makes 1¼ cups

1   lemon
1   8-ounce jar sun-dried tomatoes packed in oil, undrained
1   large roasted red pepper (optional)
2   cloves garlic, minced
5   teaspoons fresh oregano, chopped, *or* 1½ teaspoons dried oregano
½   teaspoon sugar *or* honey
    salt to taste (if not using the cheese)
2   tablespoons freshly grated Parmesan cheese *or* Cheeseless "Parmesan" Cheese *(p. 141)* (optional)

1. Wash lemon; finely grate colored portion of lemon peel. Measure 2 teaspoons lemon peel and set aside.

2. Place lemon peel, sun-dried tomatoes, roasted red pepper, garlic, oregano, and sweetener of choice in food processor. Process until almost smooth, scraping side of bowl occasionally. Add salt or Parmesan cheese and stir until well combined. (Remaining pesto can be covered and refrigerated up to one week.)

PESTO RICE AND BEANS

Serves 8
Prep. time: 10 minutes
Cooking time: 30 minutes

¼ cup walnuts

½ pound fresh green beans

1 large clove garlic

1 cup packed fresh basil leaves, rinsed

¼ cup olive oil

3½ cups water

3½ teaspoons McKay's Chicken-Style Seasoning *or* Chicken-like Seasoning *(p. 135)*

2 cups cannellini (white kidney) beans

1 cup uncooked long-grain brown rice

½ teaspoon salt (optional)

1. Preheat oven to 350°F. Spread walnuts in single layer on small, nonstick baking sheet. Bake 8 to 10 minutes until golden brown, stirring frequently.

2. Place green beans in colander; rinse well under cold running water. To prepare beans, snap off stem end from each bean, pulling off strings, if present. (Young, tender beans may not have strings.)

3. Cut green beans into 1-inch pieces; set aside.

4. To prepare basil pesto: Place garlic, basil, oil, and walnuts in food processor. Cover; process using on/off pulsing action until coarsely ground.

5. In saucepan, combine water and McKay's Chicken-Style Seasoning or Chicken-like Seasoning. Then add canned cannellini beans, with liquid, and heat thoroughly. Stir in rice; simmer, covered, for 10 minutes. Add green beans; simmer, covered, another 15 minutes, or until rice is tender.

6. Stir in basil pesto. Transfer to large serving bowl. Garnish with plum tomatoes and Italian parsley, if desired.

STIR-FRIED ASIAN VEGETABLES

Serves 6
Prep. time: 10 minutes
Cooking time: 8 minutes

MENU PLANNING TIPS

This Asian stir-fry can be served as a side dish or spooned over rice or couscous for a complete meal. Try adding tofu or any meat substitute of choice, and exchange the vegetables for ones you have on hand for variety. Remember, the stir-frying doesn't have to be limited to Chinese dishes. Use stir-fried vegetables with pasta primavera or fajitas.

¾ cup water

1 teaspoon McKay's Chicken-Style Seasoning *or* Chicken-like Seasoning *(p. 135)*

1 tablespoon cornstarch

2 tablespoons low-sodium soy sauce

½ teaspoon sugar *or* honey

1 tablespoon canola oil *or* water

1 cup carrots, diagonally sliced

1 cup celery, diagonally sliced

½ cup onions, chopped

1½ cups snow peas, trimmed

1 15-ounce can whole baby corn, drained

½ cup mushrooms, halved

1. Combine first five ingredients in a small bowl; stir with a wire whisk until well blended. Set aside.

2. Heat oil or water in a wok or large nonstick skillet over high heat. Add carrots, celery, and onions; stir-fry 2 minutes. Add snow peas, corn, and mushrooms; stir-fry 2 more minutes. Add broth mixture; stir-fry 1 minute, or until thick and bubbly.

SPRING VEGETABLE CURRY

Serves 6-8
Prep. time: 15 minutes
Cooking time: 35-45 minutes

1   recipe curry powder (below)

1   cup uncooked dried split green peas

2   medium carrots

1   medium zucchini

2½   cups water

2½   teaspoons McKay's Chicken-Style Seasoning *or* Chicken-like Seasoning *(p. 135)*

     salt to taste

1   tablespoon olive oil

2   cups onions, chopped

4   cloves garlic, minced

2   cups frozen cauliflowerets

1½   cups unsweetened coconut *or* tofu *or* soy *or* nonfat evaporated milk

¼   teaspoon crushed red pepper

½   cup fresh *or* frozen green peas

1½   cups tomatoes, seeded and chopped

6-8 cups hot cooked brown rice

MENU PLANNING TIPS

This spicy one-dish meal is for all the curry lovers out there.

CURRY POWDER:

Combine following ingredients in small bowl and mix well:

2   teaspoons ground cumin

1   teaspoon ground ginger

1   teaspoon turmeric

½   teaspoon ground cinnamon

¼   teaspoon ground mace

¼   teaspoon ground cardamom

¼   teaspoon dry mustard

1.   Prepare Curry Powder; set aside.

2.   Rinse split peas thoroughly in colander under cold running water, picking out debris and any blemished peas; set aside.

3.   Wash and peel carrots; cut into ¼-inch diagonal slices. Set aside.

4.   Cut tip and stem from zucchini; slice in half lengthwise, then cut diagonal slices ¼-inch thick. Set aside.

5.   Combine water, McKay's Chicken-Style Seasoning or Chicken-like Seasoning and 1 tablespoon Curry Powder in medium saucepan. Bring to a boil over high heat. Stir in split peas. Reduce heat to low; simmer, covered, 15 minutes.

6.   Heat oil in large skillet over medium-high heat. Add onions; cook and stir 3 minutes, or until tender. Add carrots and garlic; cook and stir 5 to 7 minutes until carrots are crisp-tender. Add to seasoned, partially cooked split peas in saucepan.

7.   Stir in cauliflowerets, milk of choice, zucchini, crushed red pepper, and salt to taste; simmer, covered, 20 to 25 minutes, until split peas are tender.

8.   Stir in green peas and tomatoes just before serving.

9.   Serve Spring Vegetable Curry over hot rice.

TERIYAKI STIR-FRY OVER RICE

2	large potatoes, chopped
2	carrots, sliced
1	tablespoon olive oil
1	small onion, chopped
½	red bell pepper, chopped
2	celery stalks, sliced
4	garlic cloves, minced
½	cup roasted peanuts *or* nuts of choice
4-6	cups cooked, long-grain brown rice

TERIYAKI SAUCE:

½	cup low-sodium soy sauce
¼	cup brown sugar *or* honey
½	tablespoon cornstarch
2	tablespoons water

1. Steam potatoes and carrots until tender. Set aside and keep warm.

2. Stir-fry over medium-high heat in a nonstick skillet in olive oil the onion, red pepper, and celery until tender, about 6 minutes. Add garlic and cook an additional 2 minutes. Add steamed potatoes and carrots and toss well. Toss in ½ cup peanuts or nuts of choice, and serve on a bed of rice.

3. To prepare Teriyaki Sauce: In small bowl combine ½ tablespoon cornstarch with 2 tablespoons water and stir until cornstarch is dissolved. Cook until sauce comes to a boil and is slightly thickened. Add more water if a thinner consistency is desired. Add soy sauce and sweetener of choice.

SUCCESSFUL STIR-FRY TIPS

1. Prepare the ingredients before heating the wok, and have them close at hand. Cut vegetables and any vegetarian meat or tofu into small, similar sizes. You can marinate the meat substitute, if desired.

2. Add the oil or water when the wok is hot. Swirl the oil or water around the bottom and sides of wok to thoroughly heat oil or water.

3. Stir-fry aromatics, such as ginger and garlic, until just fragrant. You can remove them after they've flavored the oil, or leave them in the wok.

4. Add any vegetarian meat or tofu and let it sit for a few seconds to brown before stirring. Don't crowd the pan. Cook ingredients until just done, then transfer them to a different bowl.

5. Cook the vegetables until crisp-tender. For dense vegetables, add a bit of liquid to the wok; cover, and steam.

6. Return the vegetarian meat or tofu to the wok and add a sauce that has a thickener in it, such as cornstarch *(see Stir-fried Asian Vegetables recipe, p. 88)*. Quickly toss the meat and vegetables with the sauce to cover evenly. Serve immediately.

Serves 6-8
Prep. time: 10 minutes
Cooking time: 20 minutes

MENU PLANNING TIPS

This recipe is easy to prepare, and the flavor combination is delicious. Serve it over a bed of hot rice, and top it with Teriyaki Sauce (below).

GRILLED VEGETABLES OVER RICE

Serves 6-8
Prep. time: 10 minutes
Cooking time: 10 minutes

1	green bell pepper, cut in wedges
2	carrots, thinly sliced
1	cup yellow summer squash, sliced
1	small onion, cut into wedges
2	garlic cloves, thinly sliced
1½	teaspoons olive oil
1½	teaspoons fresh oregano, chopped, *or* ½ teaspoon dried oregano
1½	teaspoons fresh basil, chopped, *or* ½ teaspoon dried basil
¼	teaspoon salt (optional)
1	large tomato, cut into eight wedges
1	cup cannellini (white kidney) beans *or* garbanzos
4	cups cooked brown rice

1. Prepare and cut vegetables. The vegetables should be approximately the same size so that they are done at the same time. The carrots should be very thin so they will be cooked enough in 10 minutes. Combine in mixing bowl all ingredients, except the tomatoes, rice, and beans. Toss vegetable mixture lightly to glaze the vegetables with olive oil, herbs, and salt.

2. Spoon vegetable mixture onto a broiler pan or cookie sheet coated with nonstick cooking spray. Broil 5 minutes; stir tomatoes and beans into vegetable mixture. Baste with additional marinade and broil for 5 additional minutes, or until vegetables are tender and lightly browned. Tomatoes and beans should be just warmed. If you prefer the tomatoes softer, add at the beginning of the 10 minutes.

3. Serve roasted vegetables over a bed of rice.

HEARTY RICE SKILLET

1	15-ounce can black beans *or* kidney beans, rinsed and drained
1	14½-ounce can crushed *or* diced tomatoes
1	cup frozen corn
½	cup frozen peas
½	cup frozen lima beans
½	cup frozen green beans, 1-inch pieces
1	cup water
¾	cup quick-cooking brown rice
½	teaspoon dried thyme *or* dillweed, crushed
	dash of bottled hot pepper sauce *or* salsa (optional)
1	8-ounce can tomato purée
1	tablespoon lemon juice
1	tablespoon sugar *or* honey
⅓	cup slivered almonds

1. Combine beans, crushed tomatoes, corn, peas, lima beans, green beans, water, uncooked rice, and thyme in a large skillet. Stir in hot pepper sauce or hot salsa, if desired. Bring to boiling; reduce heat. Simmer, covered, for 12 to 14 minutes or until rice is tender. Stir in puréed tomatoes, lemon juice, and sugar or honey; heat through.

2. Spread the almonds in a thin layer in a shallow baking pan. Bake in a 250°F oven, stirring once or twice, for 5 minutes, or until the almonds are golden.

3. To serve, stir in toasted almonds. Sprinkle with shredded mozzarella or tofu cheese.

Serves 4
Prep. time: 10 minutes
Cooking time: 15 minutes

HERBED "CHICKEN" COUSCOUS AND VEGETABLES

1	cup fresh mushrooms, sliced
1	12½-ounce can Worthington Low-Fat FriChik, chopped
	or
1	10-ounce package firm tofu, cubed
1	teaspoon olive *or* canola oil
1	cup green peas, frozen
1	tablespoon fresh parsley, chopped
½	teaspoon dried basil, crushed
⅛	teaspoon dried oregano, crushed
¼	teaspoon salt (optional)
¼	teaspoon garlic powder
⅔	cup uncooked couscous
1	medium tomato, peeled, seeded, and chopped

1. In nonstick skillet over medium-high heat, cook mushrooms and Worthington Low-Fat FriChik or tofu cubes in oil of choice until tender and lightly browned.

2. Stir in peas, parsley, basil, oregano, salt, and garlic powder, and add 1 cup water to saucepan; bring to boil. Remove from heat; stir in couscous. Cover and let stand for 5 minutes. Stir in tomatoes. Serve immediately.

Serves 4
Prep. time: 10 minutes
Cooking time: 10 minutes

MENU PLANNING TIPS

Couscous, a North African staple, is a light dish of tiny pasta made from semolina, a coarsely ground durum wheat. Serve it as you would rice or grains. In this recipe I add seasonings, mushrooms, and a chicken substitute. You can add an additional cooked vegetable on the side, a tossed green salad, and whole-grain bread to complete this meal.

GARDEN VEGETABLE COUSCOUS

Serves 8-10
Prep. time: 10 minutes
Cooking time: 15 minutes

MENU PLANNING TIPS

This pasta tastes wonderful with the garden vegetable topping and the beans and peanuts. These ingredients combine to give you a great one-dish meal. Serve with whole-grain bread and enjoy.

1	large onion, cut into thin wedges
2	cloves garlic, minced
1	teaspoon canola *or* olive oil
2	cups carrots, thinly sliced
1	teaspoon dried basil, crushed
$1/2$-1	teaspoon ground cumin, to taste
$1/4$	teaspoon salt
2	medium zucchini, quartered lengthwise and cut into $1/2$-inch pieces ($2^1/2$ cups)
1	15-ounce can garbanzo beans, rinsed and drained
1	$14^1/2$-ounce can whole tomatoes, crushed
2	teaspoons cornstarch
2	cups water
2	teaspoons McKay's Chicken-Style Seasoning *or* Chicken-like Seasoning *(p. 135)*
1	cup uncooked couscous
$1/4$	cup unsalted dry roasted peanuts, chopped in large pieces

1. Cook onion and garlic in hot oil in a large saucepan over medium-low heat till crisp-tender. Stir in carrots, $1/2$ cup water, basil, cumin, and salt; bring to boil. Reduce heat, cover, and simmer for 10 minutes.

2. Stir in zucchini, garbanzo beans, and tomatoes. Cover and cook for 2 minutes. Stir together 2 tablespoons water and cornstarch. Stir into tomato mixture. Cook and stir until thickened and bubbly. Cook and stir 2 minutes more.

3. In separate saucepan, add 2 teaspoons McKay's Chicken-Style Seasoning or Chicken-like Seasoning to 2 cups water, and bring to a boil. Add couscous; cover and let stand 5 minutes, or until liquid is absorbed; fluff with fork. Serve vegetable mixture over hot couscous. Sprinkle with peanuts before serving.

COUSCOUS ALFRESCO

Serves 4
Prep. time: 10 minutes
Cooking time: 15 minutes

2	tablespoons pine nuts *or* chopped walnuts
1	teaspoon olive oil
2	cloves garlic, minced
2	cups water
2	teaspoons McKay's Chicken-Style Seasoning *or* Chicken-like Seasoning *(p. 135)*
$1/4$	teaspoon dried basil
$1/4$	teaspoon dried oregano
2	cups uncooked whole-wheat couscous
10	fresh asparagus spears, trimmed and cut into 1-inch pieces
2	medium tomatoes, seeded and diced
$1/4$	cup ripe olives, sliced

1. In medium-size saucepan over medium heat, add pine nuts; shake pan frequently until nuts are lightly browned. Remove from saucepan; set aside.

2. Heat olive oil in same saucepan over medium heat. Add garlic; sauté 2 minutes. Add water, McKay's Chicken-Style Seasoning or Chicken-like Seasoning, basil, and oregano. Bring to a boil. Stir in asparagus. Reduce heat; cover, and simmer 1 minute. Stir in couscous; cover and remove from heat. Let stand 5 minutes.

3. Fluff couscous lightly with a fork. Stir in nuts, tomatoes, and olives. Serve immediately.

CURRIED "CHICKEN" AND BROCCOLI COUSCOUS

1	12½-ounce can Worthington FriChik, cut in thin strips
	or
1	10-ounce package firm tofu, cut in 1-inch cubes
2	teaspoons curry powder, divided
2	teaspoons olive oil, divided
½	cup onion, chopped
2	cups water
2	teaspoons McKay's Chicken-Style Seasoning *or* Chicken-like Seasoning *(p. 135)*
1½	cups broccoli florets
½	cup red bell pepper, chopped
½	cup raisins (optional)
2	teaspoons firmly packed brown sugar *or* honey ***and/or*** molasses
1	cup uncooked whole-wheat couscous

1. Sprinkle one side of FriChik strips or tofu cubes with 1 teaspoon curry powder.

2. Heat 1 teaspoon olive oil in a large skillet over medium-high heat. Add FriChik or tofu; sauté 2 minutes on each side, or until lightly browned. Remove from skillet, and keep warm.

3. Heat remaining olive oil in same skillet. Add onion; sauté 2 minutes, stirring frequently. Add water and McKay's Chicken-Style Seasoning or Chicken-like Seasoning, broccoli, red bell pepper, raisins, brown sugar or honey, remaining 1 teaspoon curry powder, and reserved FriChik or tofu to cooked onions. Bring to a boil. Stir in couscous; cover. Remove from heat; let stand 5 minutes. Toss couscous lightly with a fork before serving.

Serves 4
Prep. time: 10 minutes
Cooking time: 15 minutes

MENU PLANNING TIPS

This meal is so quick to make—your dinner is ready in 15 minutes. This dish includes your grains and vegetables all together to make a complete meal.

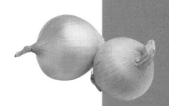

BASIL-ROASTED VEGETABLES OVER COUSCOUS

Serves 4
Prep. time: 10 minutes
Cooking time: 35 minutes

1/4   cup fresh basil, minced

2   tablespoons lemon juice

1   tablespoon olive oil

1/4   teaspoon salt

2   garlic cloves, minced

2   medium zucchini, cut into 1-inch slices

1   medium red bell pepper, cut into 1-inch pieces

1   medium yellow bell pepper, cut into 1-inch pieces

1   medium red onion, cut into eight wedges

1   cup mushrooms, halved

3   cups hot, cooked whole-wheat couscous

1.   Preheat oven to 425°F.

2.   Combine first five ingredients in a large bowl; stir well. Add zucchini, bell peppers, onion, and mushrooms; toss well to coat. Arrange vegetables in a single layer on a shallow roasting pan. Bake at 425°F for 25 to 30 minutes, or until tender and browned, stirring occasionally.

3.   Spoon roasted vegetables over couscous. Garnish with fresh basil sprigs and feta cheese, if desired.

ROASTED-PEPPER BRUSCHETTA

Serves 10
Prep. time: 30 minutes
Cooking time: 30 minutes

2   medium-size sweet red peppers

2   medium-size sweet yellow peppers

1   medium-size sweet green pepper

3   garlic cloves, unpeeled

1   medium-size loaf round Italian bread

1   tablespoon olive oil

1   tablespoon lemon juice

    fresh Parmesan cheese, grated, *or* Cheeseless "Parmesan" Cheese *(p. 141)* (optional)

1.   Heat oven to 450°F. Place whole peppers and garlic on rimmed baking sheet. Bake peppers and garlic 30 minutes, turning peppers every 10 minutes. Remove vegetables from oven. Set aside garlic and carefully place hot peppers in brown paper bag; close bag tightly, allowing peppers to steam and cool until easy to handle—about 20 minutes.

2.   Meanwhile, reduce oven temperature to 350°F. Cut bread into 11 slices, each about 1/2-inch thick. Place the two end slices on ungreased baking sheet. Cut the remaining nine slices in half and place on baking sheet. Toast bread 10 minutes, or until lightly browned.

3.   When peppers are cool, peel, halve, and seed them and chop them into 1/4-inch cubes. Peel garlic cloves. In medium-size bowl, crush garlic with back of wooden spoon. Add roasted sweet peppers, oil, and lemon juice; toss to combine. Add salt to taste, if desired.

4.   Divide pepper mixture on toasted bread. Garnish with freshly grated Parmesan cheese, if desired. Serve warm or at room temperature.

MENU PLANNING TIPS

Relish the robust flavor of Italy in this colorful appetizer, made from a pungent mixture of roasted peppers and roasted garlic. Serve over toasted Italian bread with the Pesto Risotto *(p. 98)* for an elegant light meal the next time you entertain. To shorten preparation time, use canned roasted red peppers, drained.

PESTO RISOTTO

Serves 6
Prep. time: 10 minutes
Cooking time: 25 minutes

MENU PLANNING TIPS

The Italian dish of Pesto Risotto is made with arborio rice, because it is creamy on the outside and slightly firm in the center, which is more characteristic of risotto. Serve this with Roasted-Pepper Bruschetta *(p. 97)* and tossed green salad for a light Italian dinner.

pesto (recipe below)

4½   cups water

4   teaspoons McKay's Chicken-Style Seasoning *or* Chicken-like Seasoning *(p. 135)*

2   tablespoons lemon juice

2   teaspoons olive oil

1½   cups arborio rice, uncooked

2   cloves garlic, minced

salt to taste (optional)

fresh basil sprigs

1.   Prepare pesto, set aside.

2.   In 2-quart saucepan, heat water, McKay's Chicken-Style Seasoning or Chicken-like Seasoning, and lemon juice to boiling. Remove from heat.

3.   In large skillet, heat oil over medium heat. Add rice and garlic; stir constantly for 3 minutes, or until rice starts to brown.

4.   Add ½ cup of the hot broth mixture to the sautéed rice and garlic; cook, stirring constantly, until all the liquid has been absorbed. Continue to cook, stirring constantly and adding broth mixture ½ cup at a time until all liquid has been absorbed and rice is creamy but slightly al dente—about 20 to 25 minutes. If desired, add salt to taste. Pour risotto into serving dish.

5.   Spoon pesto onto risotto in a spiral pattern; top with basil sprigs and serve immediately. (This will become sticky if allowed to stand before serving.)

PESTO:

½   cup packed fresh basil leaves, chopped

¼   cup fresh parsley sprigs, chopped

2   tablespoons pine nuts or chopped walnuts (Try toasting walnuts for a different taste.)

1   clove garlic, minced

¼   cup olive oil

1.   Place first four ingredients in the blender and process until basil, parsley, and pine nuts are chopped fine and form a paste. While machine is running, slowly pour in olive oil and process until well blended. Add freshly grated Parmesan cheese, if desired. Spoon pesto onto risotto, following previous recipe.

BASMATI RICE SEASONED
WITH DRIED FRUITS AND NUTS

1-2	tablespoons olive *or* canola oil
1	small onion, minced
$^1/_2$	cup basmati rice
$3^1/_4$	cups water
$^3/_4$	teaspoon salt
$^1/_4$	teaspoon ground cinnamon
$^1/_4$	teaspoon ground allspice
$^1/_4$	cup raisins
$^1/_4$	cup dried cranberries
$^1/_2$	cup dried apricot halves, coarsely chopped
$^1/_2$	cup pecans, toasted and coarsely chopped

Serves 6
Prep. time: 10 minutes
Cooking time: 20-30 minutes

1. Sauté in saucepan over medium heat, olive oil and onion, stirring, until soft, about 10 minutes.

2. Meanwhile, rinse the rice well and drain. When the onion is ready, add the rice, water, salt, cinnamon, allspice, raisins, cranberries, and apricots to the saucepan. Bring to a boil; reduce the heat to low, cover, and cook without stirring for 20 minutes. Do not remove the cover. After 20 minutes, uncover and check to see if the rice is tender and the water is absorbed. If not, cover and cook for a few minutes longer until the rice is done.

3. Toasting the pecans brings out the full flavor and aroma of the nuts. Preheat oven to 250°F. Spread the nuts in a single layer on a baking sheet and toast in the oven until they just begin to change color, 5 to 10 minutes. Remove from oven.

4. Add the toasted pecans to the rice and toss to combine. Transfer to a warmed serving dish and serve immediately.

VEGETABLE MEDLEY QUICHE IN RICE CRUST

Serves 6
Prep. time: 10 minutes
Cooking time: 35 minutes

3	cups cooked short-grain rice
1	tablespoon olive oil
2	stalks celery, chopped
1	medium onion, chopped
1	red bell pepper, chopped
2	garlic cloves, minced
1	zucchini *or* yellow squash, halved lengthwise and sliced
3	cups broccoli, cut into bite-size pieces
1	teaspoon McKay's Chicken-Style Seasoning *or* Chicken-like Seasoning *(p. 135)*
1	teaspoon garlic powder
1/4	teaspoon salt

TOFU FILLING:

2	cups tofu, soft
1	tablespoon lemon juice
1	tablespoon olive oil
1	tablespoon honey
2	teaspoons garlic powder
1	teaspoon dried basil
1/4	teaspoon salt
2-4	tablespoons tofu milk *or* nonfat milk

1. Prepare rice as directed on package. Short-grain rice will be stickier and hold together to form crust. Spray nonstick cooking spray into 9-inch pie plate. Press rice into pie plate to form a crust that is approximately 1/2-inch thick.

2. In nonstick skillet over medium-high heat, heat olive oil, celery, onion, and red bell pepper until tender. Add garlic and cook an additional 2 minutes. Add zucchini, broccoli, McKay's Chicken-Style Seasoning or Chicken-like Seasoning, garlic powder, and salt. Cook until vegetables are tender.

3. In blender, combine tofu filling ingredients. Blend until smooth. Add more milk of choice for pourable consistency.

4. Combine cooked vegetables and tofu mixture and mix well. Pour into rice pie shell. Bake at 375°F for 30 to 35 minutes, or until knife inserted comes out clean and filling is light brown. Serve warm.

Main Dish Dinner

POTATOES

Garden-fresh Potato Toss

Roots at 500°F

Garlic Potatoes With "Chicken"

Vegetable Potato Salad

Cheesy Potato Skins

Mexican Baked Potatoes With
Bean-and-Corn Salsa

GARDEN-FRESH POTATO TOSS

8	medium-size new potatoes, red *or* white, halved *or* quartered
1	teaspoon olive oil
1	large onion, chopped
1	red *or* green bell pepper, chopped
3	garlic cloves, minced
2	zucchini, sliced
1	yellow summer squash, sliced
1	tablespoon fresh thyme *or* ¹/₂ teaspoon dried thyme
¹/₄	teaspoon salt (optional)
	fresh thyme sprigs for garnish

1. Microwave diced potatoes in small amount of water in covered casserole dish. Cook until tender, about 12 to 15 minutes. Drain water.

2. In nonstick skillet over medium-high heat, add olive oil, onion, and pepper, and cook until tender. Add garlic, and cook additional 1 to 2 minutes. Add zucchini and yellow summer squash and cook until tender.

3. To the cooked vegetables, add the chopped cooked potatoes, thyme, and salt; mix well. Serve warm. Add additional garlic powder, if desired. (Sometimes I add McKay's Chicken-Style Seasoning or Chicken-like Seasoning for variety.) Garnish with thyme sprigs.

Serves 6
Prep. time: 10 minutes
Cooking time: 20 minutes

MENU PLANNING TIPS

This easy-to-prepare potato dish is a great one-dish meal. Add different fresh or dried herbs for a variety in flavor. Serve with a salad and whole-grain rolls for a full meal.

ROOTS AT 500°F

1	large russet potato
2	teaspoons olive oil
³/₄	cup baby carrots
1	red onion, coarsely chopped
1	yam
1	beet
2	tablespoons green onion, thinly sliced
	garlic powder to taste (optional)
	salt to taste (optional)
	parsley sprigs for garnish

1. Scrub potato and cut into ³/₄-inch cubes.

2. In 500°F oven, heat oil in a 10"x15" roasting pan until hot, about 1¹/₂ minutes. Add cubed potato, carrots, and red onion. Cook 15 minutes, stirring after 10 minutes.

3. Meanwhile, peel yam and beet; cut each into about ¹/₂-inch cubes. Add to pan after potato has cooked 15 minutes; cook about 20 minutes more, stirring every 10 minutes, until potatoes are golden brown.

4. Spoon vegetables onto a platter; garnish with parsley. Add salt and garlic powder, if desired.

Serves 4
Prep. time: 10 minutes
Cooking time: 35 minutes

MENU PLANNING TIPS

Cooking at 500°F not only helps speed up the cooking process, but also enhances the flavor of the vegetables by caramelizing the natural sugars in the vegetables, which produces an even more naturally sweet flavor.

GARLIC POTATOES WITH "CHICKEN"

Serves 6
Prep. time: 10 minutes
Cooking time: 45 minutes

MENU PLANNING TIPS
This oven-roasted meal needs only to be stirred every 10 minutes, giving you free time while it roasts.

2   pounds thin-skinned red **and/or** white potatoes (about 18)

1   tablespoon olive oil

1   onion, quartered

1   12½-ounce can Worthington Low-Fat FriChik, cubed

     or

1   10-ounce package firm tofu, cubed

1   bulb garlic, cloves peeled

3   tablespoons dried tomatoes, rehydrated and minced

2   teaspoons fresh rosemary leaves

     salt to taste (optional)

     fresh rosemary sprigs for garnish

1. Scrub potatoes. In 500°F oven, heat oil in a 10"x15" roasting pan until hot, about 1½ minutes. Add potatoes and onion; shake pan to coat vegetables with oil. Cook 15 minutes, then add FriChik or tofu cubes and garlic and cook 30 minutes more, stirring vegetables every 10 minutes.

2. Stir tomatoes and rosemary leaves into potato mixture. Add salt to taste, if desired. Pour onto serving platter and garnish with rosemary sprigs.

VEGETABLE POTATO SALAD

Serves 4
Prep. time: 10 minutes
Cooking time: 15-20 minutes

MENU PLANNING TIPS
This dish features fresh-from-the-garden vegetables. Enjoy it warm, or serve it as a chilled potato salad. The Creamy Onion-Dill Dressing can be prepared with or without dairy products.

1   cup water

½   teaspoon salt

¾   pound whole tiny new potatoes, halved **or** quartered

1   pound asparagus, cut into 1-inch pieces (1⅓ cups)

1   medium carrot, cut into thin strips (1½ cups)

     Low-Fat Creamy Onion-Dill Dressing *(p. 136)* or Nondairy Creamy Onion-Dill Dressing *(p. 137)*

     fresh dill sprigs for garnish

1. Bring water and salt to boiling in a large saucepan. Add potatoes and cook, covered, for 8 minutes. Add asparagus and carrot; cook 4 to 8 minutes more, or until potatoes are tender and asparagus and carrot strips are crisp-tender. Drain well. Arrange vegetables in a shallow serving bowl; or chill, if desired, and serve as a cold salad.

2. Prepare Creamy Onion-Dill Dressing. Add enough milk to make it quite thin and pourable. The consistency of a French dressing is about right. If it is too thick, it will overpower the taste of the vegetables. Cover and chill until serving time.

3. Just before serving, spoon dressing over vegetables. You can spoon the dressing into the middle of the vegetables, or you can toss the dressing with the vegetables, covering them evenly. Garnish with fresh dill sprigs and serve.

CHEESY POTATO SKINS

4	russet baking potatoes
1	tablespoon olive oil
1/2	teaspoon granulated garlic
	salt to taste (optional)
1/2	cup tofu cheese, grated, *or* low-fat mozzarella cheese, grated
2	tablespoons green onions *or* chives, sliced *or* chopped
1/2	cup Nondairy Creamy Onion-Dill Dressing *(p. 137)* *or* Low-Fat Creamy Onion-Dill Dressing *(p. 136)*

1. Scrub potatoes and remove any bad spots. Slice in half lengthwise. If you use potatoes that are of uniform size, the potatoes will be done at the same time. Place cut potatoes on a baking sheet. Add olive oil and toss potatoes, covering lightly with oil. Then place with cut sides up and sprinkle with garlic granules and salt. Bake at 450°F for 10 minutes; check potatoes and rotate, if some areas are more done than others. Bake an additional 20 minutes, checking at 10 minutes. When potatoes are tender and lightly browned, remove from oven.

2. Add grated cheese of choice and green onions or chives and bake an additional 5 minutes. (Or add the bean-and-corn salsa, top with the cheese, and bake 5 minutes.)

3. Serve with Creamy Onion-Dill Dressing (or nonfat sour cream on the side for dipping).

Serves 8
Prep. time: 5 minutes
Cooking time: 30 minutes

MENU PLANNING TIPS

Try serving these baked potato skins with nonfat sour cream or Tofu Sour Cream *(p. 136)*, topped with chopped chives or green onions. For variety, top these skins with chili beans or bean-and-corn salsa *(p. 107)*. With these toppings this is very filling and can serve as your main course. The cheese-topped potato skins are a great appetizer or can be served with salad to make a light meal.

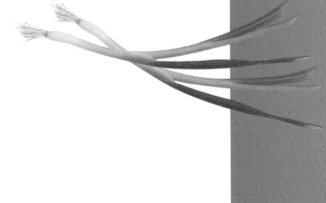

MEXICAN BAKED POTATOES
WITH BEAN-AND-CORN SALSA

4   large baking potatoes

     bean-and-corn salsa (below)

$1/2$ cup grated tofu cheese *or* low-fat shredded mozzarella cheese

$1/2$ cup Tofu Sour Cream *(p. 136)* *or* low-fat sour cream (optional)

1. Bake potatoes until tender, approximately 35 minutes. To speed up preparation time, you can microwave the baking potatoes in a covered dish with a small amount of water for approximately 15 minutes, or until just tender.

2. Split the warm potatoes in half lengthwise. Top with the bean-and-corn salsa. Sprinkle with the grated cheese of choice. Bake for 5 minutes or microwave for 1 minute to melt the cheese. Serve immediately, and top with sour cream of choice, if desired.

BEAN-AND-CORN SALSA:

1   cup canned kidney *or* pinto beans, rinsed and drained

1   cup canned cannellini (white kidney) beans, rinsed and drained

$3/4$ cup canned corn, drained, *or* fresh corn, cut off cob

$1/4$ cup red bell pepper, chopped

$1/4$ cup fresh cilantro, chopped

$1/2$ cup fresh tomatoes, chopped

2-4   tablespoons canned green chilies, chopped

2   tablespoons red onion, minced (optional)

2-4   tablespoons scallions, chopped *or* minced

1   tablespoon lemon juice

$1/2$ teaspoon ground cumin

$1/8$ teaspoon chili powder (optional)

$1/4$ teaspoon garlic powder

In medium bowl, mix all ingredients. Cover and refrigerate for at least 1 hour. The flavor is enhanced when the salsa sits for at least an hour, but it can be served immediately. There will be leftover salsa to use for other meals, so cover and chill for later use.

Serves 4
Prep. time: 15 minutes
Cooking time:
15 *or* 35 minutes

MENU PLANNING TIPS

Try delicious bean-and-corn salsa over hot baked potato halves. You can serve low-fat sour cream or Nondairy Tofu Sour Cream as an additional topping. Use these same toppings to serve leftover baked potatoes—just warm the baked potatoes and add the salsa and sour cream of choice.

Main Dish Dinner

MEXICAN & LEGUMES
Bean Enchiladas
Vegetable Burritos Grande
Baked Enchilada Casserole
White Bean Quesadillas
Layered Bean Dip
Oven-baked Vegetable Fajitas
Tamale Pie
No-Guilt Refried Beans
Mazidra
Indian Lentils and Rice

BEAN ENCHILADAS

1	16-ounce can whole tomatoes, undrained
1	medium onion, chopped (¹/₂ cup)
2	cloves garlic, minced
¹/₄	cup fresh cilantro, chopped
1	teaspoon lemon juice
2	teaspoons honey
2-4	tablespoons canned green chilies (optional)
1	large tomato, seeded and diced
1	15-ounce can pinto beans, rinsed and drained
1	cup low-fat ricotta cheese *or* substitute the following:

TOFU CHEESE RECIPE, MIXED WELL:

1	cup firm tofu, well mashed
1	tablespoon olive oil
1	tablespoon lemon juice
1	teaspoon honey
¹/₂	teaspoon salt

1	cup zucchini, peeled and grated
1	small green pepper, chopped (¹/₂ cup)
1-2	teaspoons ground cumin
6	flour tortillas (8-10 inches in diameter)
¹/₂	cup tofu cheese *or* low-fat mozzarella *or* Monterey Jack, grated (optional)

Serves 6
Prep. time: 15 minutes
Cooking time: 20 minutes

1. Heat oven to 375°F. Spray rectangular baking dish, 11" x 7" x 1¹/₂", with nonstick cooking spray. Place tomatoes, onion, and garlic in blender or food processor. Cover and blend on high speed until smooth.

2. Cook blended mixture, 2 tablespoons cilantro, lemon juice, and honey in 2-quart saucepan over medium heat for 3 minutes, stirring occasionally. Add green chilies and fresh tomato and cook an additional 1 to 2 minutes. Remove from heat.

3. Mix beans, ricotta or tofu cheese mixture, grated zucchini, green pepper, cumin, and remaining cilantro.

4. Spread ¹/₂ cup of the cooked tomato mixture in baking dish. Spoon ¹/₂ cup of the bean mixture on one side of each tortilla. Roll up tortillas; place seam sides down on tomato mixture in baking dish. Spoon remaining tomato mixture over tortillas. Sprinkle with grated cheese. Bake 20 to 25 minutes, or until tomato mixture is bubbly and cheese is melted.

VEGETABLE BURRITOS GRANDE

Serves 8
Prep. time: 10 minutes
Cooking time: 10 minutes

1 tablespoon olive oil *or* water

1 medium carrot, scraped and shredded

1 small onion, chopped

1 garlic clove, minced

1 8-ounce can tomato purée

2 cups fresh broccoli florets

2 cups canned *or* frozen corn

1 15-ounce can black beans, drained and rinsed

1-2 teaspoons chili powder

1-2 teaspoons ground cumin

1/4 teaspoon salt

dash of hot sauce (optional)

8 10-inch flour tortillas

1/2 cup tofu cheese *or* low-fat mozzarella cheese, grated (optional)

1. In large nonstick skillet with small amount of oil or water, cook carrots and onions over medium-high heat until tender. Add garlic and cook an additional 2 minutes. Stir in tomato purée, broccoli, corn, beans, chili powder, cumin, salt, and hot sauce. Cover and simmer 5 to 7 minutes.

2. Wrap flour tortillas in a paper towel and microwave on high for about 30 seconds to soften them. Keep them warm.

3. Spoon about 1/2 cup vegetable mixture evenly down center of each tortilla; sprinkle with cheese. Fold opposite sides of tortilla over filling, securing with a wooden toothpick, if necessary. Serve immediately with desired toppings of salsa *(p. 139),* nonfat sour cream or Tofu Sour Cream *(p. 136),* and/or Guacamole *(p. 140).*

BAKED ENCHILADA CASSEROLE

Serves 6-8
Prep. time: 10 minutes
Cooking time: 45 minutes

1 16-ounce can pinto beans, drained

1 16-ounce can chili beans, undrained

1 large onion, chopped

1/2-1 cup Thick and Chunky Salsa *(p. 139)* *or* Classic Fresh Salsa *(p. 139)* *or* purchased picante sauce

12 corn tortillas, cut into 1-inch squares

1-2 cups Cheeseless "Cheese" Sauce *(p. 141)* *or* low-fat cheddar cheese, grated

1 large tomato, chopped

2 cups head lettuce, chopped

Guacamole *(p. 140)*

nonfat sour cream *or* Tofu Sour Cream *(p. 136)*

1. In medium-size mixing bowl, combine beans, onion, and salsa; mix well.

2. Spray with nonstick cooking spray an 8" x 11" baking pan with 2" sides. Sprinkle 1 tablespoon water in bottom of pan. Layer pan with half of the corn tortilla pieces, half of the bean mix, and half of the cheese; repeat the layers.

3. Bake at 350°F for 45 minutes. Serve with chopped tomatoes, lettuce, guacamole, and sour cream of choice.

WHITE BEAN QUESADILLAS

2	cups canned cannellini (white kidney) beans *or* small white beans
1	cup roasted sweet red peppers, chopped
1	cup tofu cheese *or* low-fat Monterey Jack cheese, grated
½	teaspoon garlic powder
½	teaspoon dried basil
½	teaspoon dried oregano
8	large flour tortillas
1	teaspoon canola oil, divided, *or* nonstick vegetable spray

1. Warm beans and mash lightly.
2. Stir in the peppers, cheese, garlic powder, basil, and oregano.
3. Wrap the tortillas in a paper towel and microwave on high for about 30 seconds to soften them. Divide the bean mixture among the tortillas, spreading it to within 1 inch of the edges. Fold each tortilla in half.
4. In a medium nonstick skillet over medium heat, warm about ½ teaspoon of oil. Place quesadillas in the pan. Cook for 2 to 3 minutes, or until the bottoms are golden. Flip the quesadillas and gently press on them with a spatula to help the cheese melt. Cook for another 3 to 4 minutes. Remove from the pan.
5. Continue, adding the remaining oil as needed until all the quesadillas are browned. You can eliminate the oil if you spray the skillet with nonstick cooking spray between each browning.

Serves 6-8
Prep. time: 10 minutes
Cooking time: 10 minutes

MENU PLANNING TIPS
These great-tasting quesadillas work as an appetizer or can be served with salsa, guacamole, and tossed green salad for a complete meal.

LAYERED BEAN DIP

1	30-ounce can pinto beans, blended smooth
½	teaspoon ground cumin
¼	teaspoon chili powder
¼	teaspoon granulated garlic
¼	teaspoon onion powder
1	4-ounce can green chilies, chopped
1-2	cups Cheeseless "Cheese" Sauce *(p. 141)*
	chopped tomatoes *or* salsa for garnish

1. Blend beans, cumin, chili powder, garlic, and onion powder until smooth.
2. In 9-inch pie plate sprayed with nonstick cooking spray, spread an even layer of blended bean mixture. Sprinkle with chopped green chilies. Pour the uncooked Cheeseless "Cheese" Sauce over bean mixture about ¼ to ½ inch in thickness.

Serves 6
Prep. time: 5 minutes
Cooking time: 20-30 minutes

MENU PLANNING TIPS
Serve this bean dip with tortilla chips as an appetizer with any of the Mexican dishes in this section, or serve with salad as a light meal. You can also use the No-Guilt Refried Bean recipe *(p. 114)* to replace the first five ingredients. Garnish with chopped tomatoes or salsa of choice.

OVEN-BAKED VEGETABLE FAJITAS

1	medium red bell pepper, cut into 1-inch pieces
1	medium green bell pepper, cut into 1-inch pieces
2	zucchini *or* yellow squash, cut into 1-inch slices
1	large onion, cut into wedges
2	garlic cloves, thinly sliced
1	teaspoon olive oil
2	teaspoons fresh oregano, chopped, *or* ¾ teaspoon dried oregano
¼	teaspoon salt (optional)
1	large tomato, cut into eight wedges
2	cups cooked brown rice
2	cups canned chili beans
4	10-inch flour tortillas

1. Prepare and cut vegetables.

2. In mixing bowl combine peppers, squash, onion, garlic, olive oil, oregano, and salt. Toss vegetable mixture lightly to glaze the vegetables with oil and herbs.

3. Place vegetables onto a broiler pan or cookie sheet coated with nonstick cooking spray. Broil 5 minutes; add tomato wedges and stir into vegetable mixture, coating with marinade. Broil for 5 additional minutes, or until vegetables are just tender and lightly browned.

4. Assembly: Place ½ cup beans and ½ cup rice in flour tortillas. Top with grilled vegetables. Roll up tortilla and place seam-side down on serving plates. Top with salsa and sour cream of choice.

Serves 4
Prep. time: 15 minutes
Cooking time: 15 minutes

MENU PLANNING TIPS
This fajita features the flavor of grilled vegetables. Serve topped with Thick and Chunky Salsa *(p. 139)* or purchased salsa, and Tofu Sour Cream *(p. 136)* or nonfat sour cream.

TAMALE PIE

Serves 8
Prep. time: 10 minutes
Cooking time: 75 minutes

1	15-ounce can whole-kernel corn
1	15-ounce creamed corn
1	28-ounce can stewed tomatoes
1	28-ounce can tomato purée
1	can pitted olives, sliced
1	4-ounce can green chilies, chopped (optional)
3	cups uncooked cornmeal
6	teaspoons cornstarch
2	tablespoons granulated onions *or* onion powder
3	teaspoons salt
3	tablespoons honey *or* sugar
1/2	cup tofu *or* soy milk powder *or* powdered nondairy creamer
2	tablespoons oil

1. Mix all ingredients together in large mixing bowl. Put mixture in large roasting pan that has been sprayed with nonstick cooking spray. Place in oven at 450°F for 30 minutes.

2. Change oven temperature to 375°F and continue baking for 30 minutes, then cover with aluminum foil and bake an additional 15 minutes, or until cornmeal is completely cooked. Mixture becomes thick. Serve warm.

NO-GUILT REFRIED BEANS

Serves 4
Prep. time: 10 minutes
Cooking time: 10 minutes

MENU PLANNING TIPS
Serve with tacos, burritos, or chips. This is a great side dish, or an ingredient for many recipes. There is no added fat in these beans. I sometimes use this recipe with my Layered Bean Dip *(p. 111)* to replace the beans.

1	16-ounce can pinto beans, rinsed and drained
1/4	cup Thick and Chunky Salsa *(p. 139)*
2	tablespoons onion, chopped, *or* 1/2 tablespoon onion powder
1/4	teaspoon garlic powder
1/4-1/2	teaspoon ground cumin (optional)
1/4	teaspoon chili powder (optional)

1. In 2-quart saucepan over medium-high heat, combine beans, salsa, onion, garlic powder, cumin, and chili powder. Bring mixture to a boil, stirring occasionally.

2. Reduce heat to medium-low. Simmer 7 to 10 minutes, or until onion is translucent, stirring occasionally.

3. In food processor or blender, process mixture until smooth.

MAZIDRA

2	tablespoons olive oil
1-2	large onions, chopped
8	ounces dried lentils, sorted and rinsed
6-8	garlic cloves, thinly sliced *or* minced
5	cups water
1	teaspoon salt *or* to taste
1	teaspoon McKay's Chicken-Style Seasoning *or* Chicken-like Seasoning *(p. 135)*

1. In large saucepan over medium-high heat, combine olive oil and onions. Cook about 3 minutes, then add dried lentils. Cook 5 minutes, stirring constantly. Add garlic and cook an additional 5 minutes, stirring constantly. The lentils will brown slightly on the outside but should be able to be cut in half easily. The lentils are cooked just enough if a lentil breaks in half easily when you bite it.

2. Add water, salt, and McKay's Chicken-Style Seasoning or Chicken-like Seasoning and bring to a boil. Lower heat and simmer, covered, for about 30 minutes, or until lentils are tender. The lentils will not get as soft or mushy using this cooking technique. They have a nuttier flavor and texture. Serve on the side of rice, over rice, over baked potatoes, or over couscous.

Serves 6-8
Prep. time: 10 minutes
Cooking time:
30-40 minutes

MENU PLANNING TIPS

This dish features lentils with a flavor like no other lentil dish I've ever made. The dried lentils are sautéed with the onion, garlic, and olive oil, and they soak up that flavor. They maintain a crispy outside and a soft inside, changing the flavor of the lentils totally. Try this dish with rice, baked potatoes, or couscous.

INDIAN LENTILS AND RICE

1/2	cup green onions, chopped
1	tablespoon ginger, finely chopped
2-4	garlic cloves, minced
5 1/4	cups water
5	teaspoons McKay's Chicken-Style Seasoning *or* any vegetable seasoning
1 1/2	cups dried lentils, sorted and rinsed
1	teaspoon ground turmeric
1/2	teaspoon salt
1	large tomato, chopped
1/4	cup shredded coconut
2	tablespoons fresh mint leaves *or* 2 teaspoons dried mint leaves
3	cups hot cooked rice
1 1/2	cups Tofu Yogurt *(p. 136) or* fat-free plain yogurt

1. Spray 3-quart saucepan with nonstick cooking spray. Cook onions, grated ginger, and garlic in saucepan over medium heat for 3 to 5 minutes, stirring occasionally, until onions are tender.

2. Stir in 5 cups of water and McKay's Chicken-Style Seasoning or vegetable seasoning, lentils, turmeric, and salt. Heat to boiling; reduce heat. Cover and simmer about 25 to 30 minutes, adding remaining water, if needed, until lentils are tender. Stir in tomato, coconut, and mint. Serve over rice with yogurt.

Serves 6
Prep. time: 10 minutes
Cooking time: 30 minutes

MENU PLANNING TIPS

Try this Indian dish that features lentils seasoned with gingerroot and mint. Serve over rice, topped with yogurt.

Main Dish Dinner

PIZZA

Roasted Vegetable Pizza

Quick Pizza Dough

Spinach-Pesto Salad Pizza

Grilled Vegetable Pizza With
Spinach-Walnut Pesto

Pesto Pizza

Fresh Tomato-Herb Pizza

Herbed Pizza Crust

French Bread Pizza With Beans
and Chunky Vegetables

ROASTED VEGETABLE PIZZA

Serves 6
Prep. time: 20 minutes
Cooking time: 30 minutes

1	tablespoon fresh *or* 1 teaspoon dried thyme leaves
2	tablespoons lemon juice
1	teaspoon olive oil
1/4	teaspoon salt
4	small red potatoes, each cut into eight wedges
4	garlic cloves, thinly sliced
1	small yellow summer squash, cut into 1/4-inch slices
1	small red bell pepper, cut into 2-inch pieces
1	small sweet onion, cut into twelve wedges
1 1/4	cups Cheeseless "Cheese" Sauce *(p. 141)* *or* grated low-fat cheddar cheese
1	10-inch pizza crust, purchased *or* prepared from Herbed Pizza Crust *(p. 121)*, baked according to directions

1. Preheat oven to 500°F.

2. Combine thyme and remaining ingredients (except cheese and crust) in a bowl; toss well. Place vegetable mixture in 13" x 9" baking dish. Bake at 500°F for 15 minutes, stirring halfway through cooking time. Remove from oven.

3. Reduce oven temperature to 425°F. Sprinkle half of the cheese over prepared pizza crust. Arrange roasted vegetables over cheese, and top with remaining cheese. Bake at 425°F for 12 minutes, or until crust is lightly browned.

QUICK PIZZA DOUGH

Makes 1 crust
Prep. time: 15 minutes
Cooking time: 10-15 minutes

1 1/2	cups all-purpose flour
1/2	cup whole-wheat flour
1	tablespoon quick-rising yeast
1	teaspoon salt
1/2	teaspoon sugar *or* honey
1	teaspoon olive oil
3/4	cup water

1. In a food processor, combine flours, yeast, salt, and honey or sugar; pulse to mix.

2. In a small saucepan or glass measuring cup, mix oil with water and heat in microwave to 125°F to 130°F. With the processor on, gradually pour the warm liquid through the feed tube. (If the mixture is too dry, add 1 or 2 tablespoons more warm water.) Process until the dough forms a ball, then process for 1 minute to knead.

3. Transfer the dough to a lightly floured surface. Cover with plastic wrap and let rest for 10 to 15 minutes.

4. On a floured surface, use a rolling pin to roll pizza dough out to a circle that's about 12 inches in diameter and 1/2 inch in thickness. Transfer the dough to a pizza pan or a circular bake stone that has been lightly coated with cornmeal. (This prevents the crust from sticking to pan.)

5. Bake in 425°F oven for 12 to 15 minutes, or until lightly browned.

MENU PLANNING TIPS

This easy-to-make pizza dough can be used as the crust for the pizza of your choice.

SPINACH-PESTO SALAD PIZZA

SPINACH-PESTO SALAD PIZZA

Serves 4
Prep. time: 15 minutes
Cooking time: 15 minutes

4	6-inch pizza crusts, purchased *or* prepared from Herbed Pizza Crust *(p. 121)*, unbaked
1	teaspoon olive oil *or* 1 tablespoon water
1	18-ounce can Loma Linda Tender Bits, sliced
	or
10	ounces firm tofu, sautéed until browned, seasoned with garlic powder *and/or* McKay's Chicken-Style Seasoning *or* Chicken-like Seasoning *(p. 135)*
$\frac{1}{2}$	red pepper, sliced into thin, $1\frac{1}{2}$-inch-long strips
1	green onion, sliced
$\frac{1}{2}$	cup Basil-Pine Nut Pesto *(p. 138)*
6	firm-ripe Roma tomatoes, chopped
2	cups (3 ounces) firmly packed spinach leaves, rinsed and drained, cut into fine slivers
2	tablespoons lemon juice
4	tablespoons pine nuts for tossing *or* garnishing

1. Place crusts in a single layer on a 12- to 15-inch baking sheet. Bake in a 350°F oven until browned and crisp, about 15 minutes.
2. In nonstick skillet over medium heat, cook Tender Bits or tofu, red peppers, and green onions in olive oil or water until peppers are tender.
3. Prepare Basil-Pine Nut Pesto.
4. Toss well the tomatoes, spinach, pesto, and lemon juice, evenly coating the vegetables with pesto sauce. Add additional 4 tablespoons of pine nuts and mix well.
5. Place crusts on dinner plates. Top crusts with equal amounts of spinach-pesto mixture. Serve immediately.

MENU PLANNING TIPS
This salad pizza is so easy to prepare and so delicious! This is definitely a dish that family and guests are sure to enjoy. Keep purchased pizza crusts on hand, and you can toss this dinner together in no time.

GRILLED VEGETABLE PIZZA WITH SPINACH-WALNUT PESTO

Serves 6-8
Prep. time: 20 minutes
Cooking time: 10 minutes

1	12-inch pizza crust, baked
2	small zucchini, sliced lengthwise into $\frac{1}{2}$-inch-thick sticks
2	vine-ripened tomatoes, seeded and chopped (2 cups)
1	tablespoon walnut *or* olive oil
$\frac{1}{2}$	teaspoon garlic powder
$\frac{1}{2}$	teaspoon onion powder
2	tablespoons Cheeseless "Parmesan" Cheese *(p. 141)* *or* fresh Parmesan cheese

1. In a mixing bowl, toss zucchini and tomatoes in oil and season with garlic powder and onion powder. Place vegetables on a baking sheet and bake at 500°F for 8 to 10 minutes, or until tender and browned.
2. Prepare the Spinach-Walnut Pesto *(p. 139)*.
3. To assemble the pizza: Spread the pizza crust with the pesto and distribute the vegetable mixture over the top of it. Just before serving, sprinkle with Parmesan cheese of choice.

MENU PLANNING TIPS
This pizza is flavored with a delicious crust, pesto, and grilled vegetables. If the crust is made ahead, this recipe can be put together very quickly. Serve with your choice of pizza crust.

PESTO PIZZA

Serves 8
Prep. time: 10 minutes
Cooking time: 15 minutes

1	cup mushrooms, sliced
1	large red onion, chopped
1	green bell pepper, chopped
1	large tomato, seeded and chopped
1	teaspoon lemon juice
1	teaspoon sugar *or* honey
1	12-inch pizza crust, purchased *or* prepared from Herbed Pizza Crust *(p. 121)*, baked according to directions
2	teaspoons olive oil
¹/₂	cup feta cheese, crumbled, *or* tofu cheese, grated (optional)

PESTO SAUCE:

2	cups fresh basil leaves
4	peeled garlic cloves
1	tablespoon olive oil
3	tablespoons pine nuts
¹/₄	teaspoon salt
¹/₄	teaspoon McKay's Chicken-Style Seasoning *or* Chicken-like Seasoning *(p. 135)* (optional)

1. Purée all pesto sauce ingredients in food processor until smooth.

2. Spray nonstick cooking spray into nonstick skillet; heat skillet at medium-high temperature. Add mushrooms, onion, and pepper; sauté until vegetables are tender. Add tomato, and cook until tomato is warmed. (For saucier topping, cook tomato longer.) Add lemon juice and sugar or honey.

3. Brush pizza crust with olive oil and pesto sauce. Arrange vegetables on top of pizza. Top with cheese. Place on baking sheet or pizza stone. Heat for 10 to 15 minutes, or until lightly browned. Cut into eight wedges; serve hot.

FRESH TOMATO-HERB PIZZA

Serves 8
Prep. time: 20 minutes
Cooking time: 15 minutes

2	12-inch pizza crusts, purchased *or* prepared from Herbed Pizza Crust *(p. 121)*, unbaked
1	teaspoon oil
³/₄	cup onion, chopped
2	garlic cloves, minced
4¹/₂	cups plum tomatoes, chopped
2	cups yellow tomatoes, chopped (substitute with more red plum tomatoes)
¹/₂	teaspoon salt (optional)
1-2	cups Cheeseless "Cheese" Sauce *(p. 141) or* grated low-fat mozzarella cheese
2	tablespoons fresh basil, chopped, *or* 2 teaspoons dried basil, crushed
2	tablespoons fresh oregano, chopped, *or* 2 teaspoons dried oregano, crushed

Fresh Tomato Herb Pizza, continued

1. Heat 1 teaspoon oil in nonstick skillet over medium-high heat. Add onion and garlic; sauté 3 minutes, or until tender. Remove from heat; stir in plum tomatoes and salt.

2. Preheat oven to 450°F and place unbaked pizza crusts on baking sheet or pizza stone for assembly.

3. Nondairy option: Prepare Cheeseless "Cheese" Sauce. Spread half of cheese sauce over each crust, then divide the plum tomato mixture between the two pizzas, leaving ½-inch border. Divide yellow tomatoes evenly between pizzas.

LOW-FAT DAIRY OPTION:

Spread plum tomato mixture evenly over prepared crusts, leaving a ½-inch border. Divide yellow tomatoes evenly between pizzas, and sprinkle each pizza with 1 cup of low-fat cheese.

4. Bake at 450°F for 12 to 15 minutes, or until lightly browned. Remove pizzas to cutting boards; let stand 5 minutes. Sprinkle each pizza with 1 tablespoon fresh basil and 1 tablespoon fresh oregano; slice and serve.

HERBED PIZZA CRUST

1	tablespoon honey
1	package (1⅓ tablespoons) active dry yeast
1	cup warm water (105°F to 115°F)
2½	cups all-purpose flour *or* whole-wheat flour
½	cup yellow cornmeal
1	tablespoon fresh thyme, chopped
1	teaspoon fresh rosemary, chopped
½	teaspoon fresh oregano, chopped
¼	teaspoon salt
2	teaspoons olive oil
2	tablespoons cornmeal

1. Dissolve honey and yeast in warm water in a small bowl; let stand 5 minutes.

2. Place flour, ½ cup cornmeal, thyme, rosemary, oregano, and salt in a food processor; pulse 2 times, or until blended. With processor on, slowly add yeast and water mixture and 2 teaspoons of oil through food chute. Process until dough leaves sides of bowl and forms ball. Process 1 additional minute.

3. Turn dough onto a lightly floured surface and knead for 2 minutes. Place dough in a large bowl, coated with nonstick cooking spray, turning dough to coat top. Cover dough and let rise in a warm place (85°F), free from drafts, for 1 hour, or until doubled in bulk. (For small amounts of dough, I use the microwave with the door closed.)

4. Punch down risen dough and divide in half. Roll each half of dough into a 12-inch circle on a lightly floured surface. Place divided dough on two 12-inch pizza pans, baking sheets, or baking stones that are coated with nonstick cooking spray and sprinkled with 1 tablespoon cornmeal. Crimp edges of dough with fingers to form a rim around the edge.

5. Bake in preheated oven at 425°F for 10 to 12 minutes if recipe calls for a precooked crust. In some pizza recipes the toppings are added directly to the unbaked pizza dough and both are baked together. Consult recipes before baking the plain crust.

Makes two 12-inch crusts
Prep. time: 60 minutes
Cooking time: 10-12 minutes

MENU PLANNING TIPS
Use as the crust for any of the pizza recipes in this section. Top with any combination of toppings, as you would for traditional pizza. For variety, try adding fresh garlic cloves (minced or thinly sliced), sun-dried tomatoes, basil, or other herbs to this pizza crust.

FRENCH BREAD PIZZA WITH BEANS AND CHUNKY VEGETABLES

CRUST:

4   5-inch-long pieces of French *or* Italian bread

TOPPING:

2   cups chunky vegetable tomato sauce, purchased, *or* Chunky Vegetable Sauce *(p. 78)*

1   15$\frac{1}{2}$-ounce can pinto *or* cannellini (white kidney) beans, drained and rinsed

$\frac{1}{2}$ small red onion, halved and thinly sliced

2-4   tablespoons fresh basil, chopped, *or* $\frac{1}{2}$ teaspoon dried basil

$\frac{1}{8}$ teaspoon garlic powder

2   cups Cheeseless "Cheese" Sauce *(p. 141)* *or* grated, reduced-fat, part-skim mozzarella cheese

fresh chopped basil for garnish

1. Preheat oven to 425°F. Line a large cookie sheet with foil; spray with nonstick cooking spray.

2. Cut each piece of bread in half horizontally. Hollow out center of each to form $\frac{3}{4}$-inch-thick shell. Save bread crumbs for another use. If necessary, cut thin slice off rounded bottom of each piece so it will sit firmly while baking. Place on cookie sheet, hollowed side up. Set aside.

3. In large bowl, combine Chunky Vegetable Sauce, beans, onion, basil, and garlic powder; mix well. Divide mixture evenly among shells, spreading almost to edges. Spoon cheese sauce over tomato layer, or sprinkle with grated cheese. Top cheese layer with additional chopped fresh basil, if desired.

4. Bake at 425°F for 15 minutes, until cheese sauce is bubbly or the sprinkled cheese is melted and lightly browned, and the filling is hot.

Serves 8
Prep. time: 15 minutes
Cooking time: 12-15 minutes

Dessert

Peanut Butter Cookies

Glazed Fresh Strawberry Pie

Pumpkin Pie

Blueberry Crisp

Fresh Apple-Pineapple
Cream Pie

Glazed Fresh Peach Pie

Pastry Crust

Low-Fat Raspberry
Cheesecake

Strawberry-Almond Torte

PEANUT BUTTER COOKIES

1	cup applesauce
1/4	cup canola oil
1	banana
1	cup peanut butter
1	cup brown sugar
1	cup all-purpose flour *or* whole-wheat flour
1/2	teaspoon salt
2	tablespoons water
2 1/2	cups all-purpose flour *or* whole-wheat flour
2	teaspoons baking soda
6	tablespoons cornstarch

1. Place applesauce, oil, and banana in blender or food processor and process until smooth and slightly foamy. Place in large mixing bowl.
2. Add peanut butter, brown sugar, 1 cup flour, salt, and water. Mix well.
3. Add additional flour, baking soda, and cornstarch. Mix well.
4. Place cookie dough by rounded teaspoonfuls on ungreased cookie sheet. Dip fork in water and flatten each mound of cookie dough to form a cookie that's approximately 1/2 inch in thickness.
5. Bake at 325°F for 12 to 15 minutes, or until top is light brown. Edges and bottoms should be golden brown, and the centers should still be slightly soft. When cookies cool, they will get harder, so if you like soft cookies, undercook them slightly. If you like crispy cookies, cook the full 15 minutes.

Makes:
five dozen 2 1/2-inch cookies
Prep. time: 10 minutes
Cooking time: 12-15 minutes

RECIPE TIPS

This cookie recipe contains no milk, eggs, or shortening. Applesauce and a banana replace the shortening. Crunchy peanut butter can be used if you like peanut pieces in your cookies. You can replace brown sugar with 1 cup honey and add to liquid mixture in blender, processing until smooth and foamy. Delete water if using honey.

GLAZED FRESH STRAWBERRY PIE

1	9-inch Pastry Crust *(p. 129)*, baked
6	cups fresh strawberries, hulled
1	cup water
2	tablespoons cornstarch
2	tablespoons cool water
1/4	cup sugar *or* honey
	red food coloring *or* grape juice for color (optional)

1. Prepare Pastry Crust according to directions.
2. Place 1 cup of strawberries and 1 cup of water in food processor or blender. Cover and process or blend till mixture is smooth. Transfer to a small saucepan. Bring to a boil; simmer 2 minutes.
3. Whisk together cornstarch and 2 tablespoons water until cornstarch is dissolved. Add honey or sugar. Stir into blended berry mixture. Cook and stir over medium heat till mixture is thickened and bubbly. Cook and stir 2 minutes more. Remove from heat. Stir in red food coloring or grape juice to tint a rich red color. Cool to room temperature.
4. Fold remaining fresh strawberries into cooled sauce mixture. Pour into baked pie shell. Cover and chill for 3 to 4 hours or until set. Serve garnished with nondairy whipped topping of choice.

Serves 8
Prep. time: 10 minutes
Cooking time: 15 minutes

RECIPE TIPS

If you prefer, you can delete the water and sugar or honey and use apple juice concentrate as you would the water. The juice provides the liquid and the sweetener for the pie. Garnish with nondairy whipped topping or Tofu Whipped Cream *(p. 136)*.

PUMPKIN PIE

Serves 16
Makes two 9-inch pies
Prep. time: 10 minutes
Cooking time: 80 minutes

RECIPE TIPS

No one will even notice that the eggs and milk have been replaced with more nutritious ingredients. Serve with nondairy whipped topping or Tofu Whipped Cream (p. 136).

2	uncooked Pastry Crusts (p. 129)
1	29-ounce can Libby's pumpkin
4	tablespoons cornstarch
3/4	cup water
1 1/2	cups sugar
1	teaspoon salt
2	teaspoons cinnamon
1	teaspoon ginger
1	teaspoon cloves
1/2	cup Soyagen (soy milk powder) *or* nondairy creamer powder
2 1/2	cups water
1	cup all-purpose flour

1. Preheat oven to 425°F.

2. Empty can of pumpkin into large mixing bowl.

3. In small bowl, whisk together cornstarch and cool water until cornstarch is dissolved. Add to pumpkin and mix well. Add 3/4 cup water, sugar, salt, cinnamon, ginger, and cloves. Mix well.

4. Mix together milk powder of choice and 2 1/2 cups water until dissolved. Add to pumpkin mixture. Mix well. Add flour and mix.

5. Pour pumpkin mixture into two 9-inch pie shells. If baking both pies at once, place one pie on bottom rack of oven and one on top rack, and place aluminum foil loosely over each pie. Halfway through baking time, exchange the pies' oven position. If baking only one pie, place it on lower rack and place foil over top rack to prevent the crust and pie top from overbrowning. Bake for 15 minutes at 425°F, then lower the temperature to 350°F for the remaining time. For the last 10 minutes, remove the foil and lightly brown piecrust.

BLUEBERRY CRISP

Serves 10
Prep. time: 10 minutes
Cooking time: 40 minutes

RECIPE TIPS

This recipe can be made with your choice of fruits and topped with the delicious crisp topping. Serve with nondairy whipped topping or Tofu Whipped Cream (p. 136).

1	12-ounce can frozen apple juice concentrate, undiluted
2	tablespoons cornstarch
1	tablespoon margarine (optional)
1	teaspoon lemon juice
1	teaspoon cinnamon
6	cups fresh *or* frozen blueberries

CRUMB TOPPING:

1/4	cup canola oil
1/3	cup honey
1/2	cup pecans, chopped
1/2	cup all-purpose *or* whole-wheat flour
2	cups quick-cooking oats

Blueberry Crisp, continued

1. In large saucepan or skillet, combine thawed apple juice concentrate and corn-starch; whisk together until completely dissolved. Cook over medium heat until thickened. Add margarine, lemon juice, and cinnamon. Stir to blend ingredients. Remove mixture from heat, pour over blueberries, and toss well.

2. To prepare crumb topping: In medium-size mixing bowl, cream together oil and honey. Add chopped nuts, flour, and oats. Toss well, coating all dry ingredients with the oil-and-honey mixture.

3. In 9" x 13" baking dish sprayed with nonstick cooking spray, place the blueberry filling. Sprinkle crumb topping evenly over the fruit. Bake in 350°F oven for 30 to 40 minutes, or until crumb topping is golden brown and the filling is bubbling. Serve warm with whipped topping of choice.

FRESH APPLE-PINEAPPLE CREAM PIE

1   9-inch Pastry Crust *(p. 129)*, baked
5   large Golden Delicious apples, grated

NONDAIRY OPTION:

1½   cups firm tofu
1-2   tablespoons canola oil
1   tablespoon lemon juice
¼-½   teaspoon lemon rind, grated
2-4   tablespoons honey
1   teaspoon vanilla
½   teaspoon salt
1   16-ounce can crushed pineapple, slightly drained

DAIRY OPTION:

2   cups nonfat pineapple yogurt
1   16-ounce can crushed pineapple, drained

1. Prepare Pastry Crust according to directions.

2. For nondairy option: Blend the tofu, oil, lemon juice, lemon rind, honey, vanilla, and salt until smooth and creamy. If mixture is too thick to blend, add pineapple juice from the canned pineapple one tablespoon at a time to make mixture blendable. Stir in canned pineapple and grated apples.

   For dairy option: Mix together purchased nonfat pineapple yogurt, canned pineapple, and grated apple.

3. Pour pie filling into cooled pastry crust. Cover and chill approximately 2 hours to set.

Serves 8
Prep. time: 10 minutes
Cooking time: 10-12 minutes

RECIPE TIPS

You can use any flavor yogurt to change the flavor of this pie. The tofu pie filling can also be made with your choice of fresh fruits added for variety in flavor. Garnish with nondairy whipped topping or Tofu Whipped Cream *(p. 136)* and slivered almonds just before serving.

GLAZED FRESH PEACH PIE

1   9-inch Pastry Crust *(recipe below)*, baked

6   cups fresh peaches, pitted, peeled, and cut in wedges

1   cup water

2   tablespoons cornstarch

2   tablespoons cool water

$\frac{1}{4}$ cup sugar *or* honey

1. Prepare Pastry Crust according to directions. To make the checkerboard edge, as shown, use a sharp knife to cut across the rim at $\frac{1}{2}$-inch intervals. Fold every other piece in toward the center.

2. Place 1 cup peaches and 1 cup water in food processor or blender. Cover and process or blend till mixture is smooth. Transfer to a small saucepan. Bring to a boil; simmer 2 minutes.

3. Whisk together cornstarch and 2 tablespoons water until cornstarch is dissolved. Add honey or sugar. Stir into peach mixture. Cook and stir over medium heat till mixture is thickened and bubbly. Cook and stir 2 minutes more. Remove from heat. Cool to room temperature.

4. Fold remaining fresh peaches into cooled sauce mixture. Turn into baked pie shell. Cover and chill for 3 to 4 hours or until set.

Serves 8
Prep. time: 10 minutes
Cooking time: 10-12 minutes

RECIPE TIPS
This recipe is a delicious presentation of fresh peaches. You can use blueberries or any other fresh fruit with this glaze. If you prefer, you can delete the water and sugar or honey and use apple juice concentrate as you would the water. The juice provides the liquid and the sweetener for the pie. Garnish with nondairy whipped topping or Tofu Whipped Cream *(p. 122)*.

PASTRY CRUST

$1\frac{1}{4}$ cups all-purpose flour

$\frac{1}{4}$ teaspoon salt

$\frac{1}{3}$ cup canola oil

4   tablespoons cold water

1. Sift flour and salt. Whisk cold water into oil until emulsified. Pour oil mixture into dry mixture. Stir quickly with fork until flour is coated with oil mixture. To prevent a tough crust, be careful not to handle pastry dough too much.

2. Roll out pastry dough between two pieces of waxed paper until it is 2 inches larger than the diameter of the pie plate you are using. Peel off the top piece of waxed paper and lay rolled pastry over the pie or tart pan. Remove waxed paper and fit crust into the pan, removing all air bubbles. Finish the edge according to your preference. If using a tart pan, use your fingers to seal the top edge of crust tightly to the pan to keep crust from falling in as it bakes.

3. If you are baking the crust without a filling, be sure to prick the bottom and sides of the uncooked crust liberally with a fork to prevent air bubbles and falling edges. Bake in 450°F oven for 12 to 15 minutes, or till pastry is golden. Cool on a wire rack.

Makes 1 crust
Prep. time: 5 minutes
Cooking time: 12-15 minutes

RECIPE TIPS
Options for crust: You can decrease flour by 2 tablespoons and replace it with toasted wheat germ. This works well when using the crust for a main dish recipe. If baking the crust without filling, decrease the oil by 1 tablespoon. If you like a thicker crust, you can layer this piecrust by rolling out one crust and then placing another rolled-out crust directly on top of the first one. This also makes a great top crust for hearty potpies or fruit pies.

LOW-FAT RASPBERRY CHEESECAKE

1	cup fresh *or* loose-pack frozen raspberries
1	cup all-purpose flour *or* whole-wheat flour
1	teaspoon baking powder
1/2	cup sugar *or* honey
1/4	cup canola oil
1	tablespoon cornstarch
3	tablespoons water
1	teaspoon vanilla
1	cup plain fat-free yogurt *or* Tofu Yogurt (below)
1/4	cup sugar *or* honey
1	tablespoon cornstarch
3	tablespoons water
2	tablespoons all-purpose flour
1 1/2	teaspoons lemon peel, finely shredded
1	teaspoon vanilla

Serves 12
Prep. time: 15 minutes
Cooking time: 35 minutes

RECIPE TIP
Serve with Tofu Yogurt (below).

1. Spray a 9-inch springform pan with nonstick cooking spray; set aside. Thaw frozen raspberries at room temperature for 15 minutes. Drain, if necessary.

2. Combine flour, baking powder, and sugar (if using sugar).

3. In separate mixing bowl, combine oil and honey (if using instead of sugar). In small cup, whisk 1 tablespoon cornstarch into 3 tablespoons water. Add the cornstarch mixture to the oil mixture. Add 1 teaspoon vanilla and mix well. Combine flour mixture with liquid mixture. Spread onto bottom of prepared pan; sprinkle with loose raspberries.

4. Combine the yogurt of choice, 1/4 cup sugar or honey, 1 tablespoon cornstarch, 3 tablespoons water, 2 tablespoons flour, lemon peel, and 1 teaspoon vanilla in medium mixing bowl. Mix till smooth; pour over berries-and-cream mixture.

5. Bake in a 350°F oven about 45 to 50 minutes, or until center appears set when shaken gently. Cool in pan on a wire rack for 15 minutes. Loosen and remove sides of pan. Cool completely. Cover and chill for 2 to 24 hours before serving.

TOFU YOGURT:

1	cup firm tofu
2	tablespoons canola oil
1	tablespoon lemon juice
1 1/2	teaspoons honey
1	teaspoon vanilla
1/2	teaspoon salt

Makes 1 1/4 cups

Combine all ingredients in a blender or food processor. Blend until smooth and creamy. Chill until serving.

STRAWBERRY-ALMOND TORTE

CRUST INGREDIENTS:

¼	cup canola oil
¼-½	cup sugar *or* honey
2	egg whites *or* 2 tablespoons cornstarch, mixed with 6 tablespoons water
1	teaspoon vanilla
2	cups all-purpose *or* whole-wheat flour
¼	teaspoon salt
¼	cup almonds, thinly sliced *or* chopped (optional)

ALMOND FILLING FOR CRUST:

2	egg whites *or* 2 tablespoons cornstarch, mixed with 6 tablespoons water
¼	cup sugar *or* honey
½	teaspoon almond extract
1	teaspoon pure vanilla extract
½	cup almond paste (available in specialty section of grocery store)

WHIPPED TOPPING:

4	cups 1 percent tofu, soft
½	cup canola oil
½	cup honey
2	teaspoons lemon juice
½	teaspoon salt
6	teaspoons vanilla

OR

4	cups nondairy whipped topping *(as substitute for tofu whipped topping)*

FRESH FRUIT FILLING:

1	quart fresh strawberries

1. To make crust: Whisk together oil and honey or sugar until frothy. Add egg whites or cornstarch and water mixture to the oil/honey mixture and whisk again. (Be sure cornstarch is well dissolved in the water before adding to oil mixture.) Add vanilla and mix well. Stir in flour, salt, and almonds. Divide crust ingredients and spread into two 9-inch round pans, half in each pan. Set aside. Preheat oven to 350°F.

2. To make almond filling: Beat egg whites or water and cornstarch until foamy. Gradually add sugar or honey, vanilla, and almond extract and beat together well. Blend in the almond paste and mix well. Spread half of filling on top of each uncooked crust.

3. Bake crust with almond filling at 350°F for 25 to 30 minutes. Cool 5 minutes before removing from the pans. Turn over pans to remove crust and let cool on cooling racks.

4. To make whipped topping: Blend all ingredients—tofu, oil, honey, lemon juice, salt, and vanilla—until smooth and creamy. Chill until serving.

5. To prepare fresh strawberry filling: Wash and stem the berries and leave half of the nicest looking ones whole for the top of the torte. Cut the rest of the berries in half to be used in the center of the torte.

6. To assemble the torte: Place one of the cooled crusts on a cake plate. Spread with half the whipped topping. Place the halved strawberries on top of the whipped topping. Top with the remaining crust. Spread the top of the crust with the remaining whipped topping. Top with the whole strawberries, turned stem-side down, placed closely together so that they cover the entire top of the crust. Serve immediately.

Serves 12
Prep. time: 20 minutes
Cooking time: 30 minutes

RECIPE TIPS

This recipe should be assembled just before serving. If you make this for company, prepare the crusts and have them cooled and ready for assembly. Make the whipped topping (below) and have it chilling in the refrigerator, or use purchased nondairy whipped topping. Wash and prepare the strawberries and chill until ready to serve. Having made these preparations, you can assemble the torte in 5 minutes. This prevents the crust from becoming soggy.

Many people on special diets because of allergies or illness may not be able to tolerate some spices or seasonings such as chili powder and vinegar. Others may be allergic to milk products or may be following a vegan vegetarian diet, eliminating these foods.

This section has nondairy options for mayonnaise, salad dressings, and cheeses. It also has substitutions for some of the seasonings and spices that are not tolerated by some people. There is even a ketchup recipe without vinegar. You'll love the pesto sauces that are made without cheese. Try these delicious substitutions and variations that will not leave you feeling deprived.

Variations & Substitutions

Cinnamon Substitute

Chili Powder Substitute

Chicken-like Seasoning

Tofu Whipped Cream

Tofu Yogurt or Sour Cream

Low-Fat Creamy Onion-Dill Dressing

Ranch Soy Mayonnaise

Nondairy Creamy Onion-Dill Dressing

Creamy Herb Dressing

Creamy Cucumber Dressing

Basil-Pine Nut Pesto

Spinach-Walnut Pesto

Thick and Chunky Salsa

Classic Fresh Salsa

Guacamole

Tartar Sauce

Sweet-and-Sour Sauce

Vinegar-free Tomato Ketchup

Cheeseless "Parmesan" Cheese

Cheeseless "Cheese" Sauce

CINNAMON SUBSTITUTE

Use coriander seed in equal amounts to cinnamon, *or* use 1 part coriander seed and 1 part anise seed, *or* use 3 parts coriander seed and 1 part sweet anise seed. Grind to a powder in an electric Moulinex, or by hand with a mortar and pestle. Use in place of cinnamon.

CHILI POWDER SUBSTITUTE

Makes 6 tablespoons

1	tablespoon paprika
1	teaspoon cumin
2	bay leaves
1	tablespoon sweet basil
1	tablespoon dried bell pepper
1	tablespoon parsley flakes
1	teaspoon ground dillweed *or* ¹/₂ teaspoon dill seed
1	teaspoon oregano
1	tablespoon onion powder

Grind all ingredients to fine powder in an electric Moulinex, or by hand with mortar and pestle. Store in well-cleaned seasoning container.

CHICKEN-LIKE SEASONING

Makes ¹/₂ cup

¹/₃	cup nutritional yeast flakes
³/₄	teaspoon dried green bell pepper
¹/₄-¹/₂	teaspoon salt
¹/₂	teaspoon dried celery flakes
¹/₂	teaspoon garlic powder
1	teaspoon onion powder
¹/₂	teaspoon sage
¹/₂	teaspoon thyme
¹/₄	teaspoon marjoram
1	tablespoon parsley flakes

Mix ingredients and grind to a powder in an electric Moulinex, or by hand with mortar and pestle. Store in sealed container.

TOFU WHIPPED CREAM

Makes 1½ cups
Prep. time: 5 minutes

RECIPE TIPS
This whipped cream alternative contains no cholesterol or saturated fat. If you use firm tofu in this recipe, you will need to add a few tablespoons of water to thin the cream to a blendable consistency. This whipped cream can be made up to three days in advance and chilled until needed.

1	10-ounce container 1 percent tofu, soft
2	tablespoons canola oil *or* olive oil
2	tablespoons honey
½	teaspoon lemon juice
⅛	teaspoon salt
1½	teaspoons vanilla

Combine all ingredients in blender or food processor and process until smooth and creamy. Chill and serve as you would whipped cream.

TOFU YOGURT OR SOUR CREAM

Makes 1¼ cups
Prep. time: 5 minutes

RECIPE TIPS
This nondairy alternative can be used whenever a recipe calls for yogurt or sour cream. It can be made ahead and chilled up to five days.

1	10-ounce container 1 percent tofu, soft
2	tablespoons canola oil
1	tablespoon lemon juice
1½	teaspoons honey
½	teaspoon salt

Combine all ingredients in blender or food processor and blend until smooth. Chill until serving.

LOW-FAT CREAMY ONION-DILL DRESSING

Makes approximately
½ cup

¼	cup fat-free mayonnaise *or* salad dressing
¼	cup fat-free plain yogurt *or* tofu yogurt
1	tablespoon lemon juice
¼	teaspoon onion powder
2	green onions, thinly sliced (2 tablespoons) *or* 2 teaspoons chives, chopped
2	teaspoons fresh dill, chopped *or* ½ teaspoon dried dillweed

Combine all ingredients in small bowl. Cover and chill.

RANCH SOY MAYONNAISE

Makes 2 cups
Prep. time: 5 minutes

1	cup water
$^2/_3$	cup Soyagen (soy milk powder)
1	pinch salt (optional)
1	tablespoon honey *or* sugar
2-4	tablespoons Hidden Valley Ranch dressing mix
$^1/_4$	cup light olive oil *or* canola oil
	juice of 1 fresh lemon

1. In blender, place water, Soyagen,* salt, honey or sugar, and ranch dressing mix, and process until smooth.

2. While continuing to blend, slowly pour oil into mixture. Mixture will thicken. Pour into container that has sealable lid.

3. Stir lemon juice into mayonnaise mixture. The mayonnaise will thicken. Chill in sealed container until serving time.

If you do not have access to Soyagen, a soy milk powder, do not use any other soy or tofu milk powder, because the mayonnaise will not thicken. It is best to replace the water and Soyagen with 10 ounces of soft tofu, blended with enough water to thin to white-sauce consistency.

RECIPE TIPS

This soy mayonnaise tastes very much like the traditional ranch dressing. Use this recipe as a substitute for mayonnaise on sandwiches, topping for baked potatoes or vegetables, and for potato, chicken, or pasta salads. This mayonnaise contains no cholesterol.

NONDAIRY CREAMY ONION-DILL DRESSING

Makes 1 cup

$^1/_2$	cup tofu, soft
2	tablespoons tofu *or* soy milk
2	tablespoons olive oil
2-3	teaspoons lemon juice
1	teaspoon honey
$^1/_4$	teaspoon salt
$^1/_4$	teaspoon garlic powder
$^1/_4$	teaspoon onion powder
2	green onions, thinly sliced (2 tablespoons), *or* 2 teaspoons chives, chopped
2	teaspoons fresh dill, chopped, *or* $^1/_2$ teaspoon dried dillweed

1. Put all the above ingredients, except the green onions or chives and dill, in the blender and blend until smooth. Scrape sides of blender as needed.

2. Pour into bowl and stir in green onions or chives and dill. (Any fresh herb can be substituted for variety.) Add more lemon juice if a tangier taste is preferred. Cover and chill.

RECIPE TIPS

This recipe makes a thick dip that is like a sour cream-based onion dip. It's great served with baked potatoes, potato skins, potato salad, and even can be used as a spread on bread. Thin it with more milk, to the consistency of French dressing, when using it in recipes such as Vegetable Potato Salad *(p. 104)* and Cheesy Potato Skins *(p. 105)*.

Makes 1 cup
Prep. time: 5 minutes

RECIPE TIPS

This dressing can be made thinner so it is pourable, or thicker if used for a dip. It can be made with any variety of herbs, preferably fresh herbs for the best flavor.

Makes 1¹/₂ cups
Prep. time: 5 minutes

RECIPE TIPS

Use this dressing with Middle Eastern dishes, Lentil Patties *(p. 56)*, or with any sandwiches or salads. Store in airtight container until serving.

Makes 1 cup
Prep. time: 5 minutes

RECIPE TIPS

Use tossed into pasta, on pizza crust, garlic bread, salad greens, or on potatoes. If fresh basil is not available, use fresh spinach leaves or fresh parsley leaves, and then use 2 to 4 teaspoons dried basil.

CREAMY HERB DRESSING

¹/₂	cup 1 percent tofu, soft
2	tablespoons tofu *or* soy *or* nonfat milk
2	tablespoons olive oil
2-3	tablespoons lemon juice
1	teaspoon honey
¹/₄	teaspoon salt
¹/₄	teaspoon garlic powder
2	teaspoons fresh dill *or* ¹/₂-1 teaspoon dried dill

1. Combine all ingredients except the dill in the blender and blend until smooth. Scrape the sides of the blender as needed. Add more milk as needed to get a consistency that is quite thin and pourable.

2. Pour into bowl and stir in dill. Add more lemon juice if a tangier taste is preferred.

CREAMY CUCUMBER DRESSING

¹/₂	cup tofu, soft
2	tablespoons tofu *or* soy *or* nonfat milk
2	tablespoons olive oil
2-3	teaspoons lemon juice
1	teaspoon honey
¹/₄	teaspoon salt
1	garlic clove, minced, *or* ¹/₄ teaspoon garlic powder
2	teaspoons fresh dill *or* ¹/₂-1 teaspoon dried dill
¹/₄	cucumber, peeled and grated, *or* chopped fine

1. Place the first seven ingredients in the blender and blend until smooth. Scrape sides of blender as needed. Add more milk as needed to get a consistency that is quite thin and pourable. A thinner consistency best blends the flavors of the food it's served with.

2. Pour into bowl and stir in dill and cucumber (fresh dill is preferred). Add more lemon juice if a tangier taste is preferred.

BASIL-PINE NUT PESTO

¹/₃-¹/₂	cup fresh basil leaves
¹/₃	cup pine nuts
2	cloves garlic
¹/₄-¹/₂	cup olive oil
1	teaspoon lemon juice
¹/₄	teaspoon McKay's Chicken-Style Seasoning *or* Chicken-like Seasoning *(p. 135)* (optional)
	salt to taste (optional)

In blender or food processor combine basil leaves, nuts, and garlic cloves and process until finely chopped. Continue to scrape sides of container between blending. With machine running, pour in olive oil in a thin stream. Add lemon juice. Add McKay's Chicken-Style Seasoning and salt to taste, if desired. Process briefly until well mixed.

SPINACH-WALNUT PESTO

2	cups packed spinach leaves
2	tablespoons fresh basil leaves *or* 2 teaspoons dried basil
$\frac{1}{4}$	cup toasted walnuts
2-3	cloves garlic, peeled and chopped
$\frac{1}{4}$	cup nonfat yogurt *or* Tofu Yogurt *(p. 136)*
1	tablespoon walnut *or* olive oil
$\frac{1}{4}$	teaspoon lemon juice

1. Wash and prepare spinach leaves and fresh basil.
2. Toast walnuts in 350°F oven for 8 to 10 minutes.
3. In a food processor, combine spinach, basil, walnuts, and garlic. Pulse until very finely chopped. Add yogurt, oil, and lemon juice; process until smooth.

Makes 2 cups
Prep. time: 10 minutes

RECIPE TIPS
This delicious pesto is made with spinach leaves and basil. It is a great sauce tossed with pasta, served on garlic bread, pizza crust, potatoes, or salad.

THICK AND CHUNKY SALSA

3	$14\frac{1}{2}$-ounce cans diced tomatoes
1	$14\frac{1}{2}$-ounce can tomato sauce *or* purée
1	large onion, chopped
3-5	fresh jalapeño peppers, chopped (use less if you prefer milder salsa)
$\frac{1}{2}$	cup lemon juice
5	cloves garlic, minced
	salt to taste (optional)
$\frac{1}{2}$	bunch fresh cilantro, chopped

1. Place two cans of diced tomatoes in blender and process just a few seconds.
2. In medium-size saucepan, add partially blended tomatoes and the third can of diced tomatoes, tomato sauce or purée, onion, jalapeño peppers, lemon juice, garlic, and salt. Cook 10 to 20 minutes, or until salsa comes to a boil. Let cool. Add fresh cilantro. Place in sealed container and refrigerate until serving time.

Makes approximately
$3\frac{1}{2}$ cups

CLASSIC FRESH SALSA

$1\frac{1}{2}$	cups ripe tomatoes, chopped
$\frac{1}{4}$	cup green onions, sliced thin
2-4	tablespoons canned green chilies, chopped
$\frac{1}{4}$	cup fresh cilantro, chopped (optional)
$1-1\frac{1}{2}$	teaspoons lemon juice
	salt to taste (optional)

Prepare vegetables and mix together. Serve chilled.

Makes $1\frac{2}{3}$ cups
Prep. time: 10 minutes

GUACAMOLE

Makes 1¼ cups

2 ripe avocados, peeled and pitted

1½ tablespoons fresh lime juice

¼ teaspoon garlic powder

¼ teaspoon salt (optional)

1 tablespoon fresh cilantro, chopped

In a bowl, coarsely mash avocados with a fork or pastry blender. Stir in lime juice, garlic powder, salt, and fresh cilantro.

TARTAR SAUCE

Makes 2½ cups

1 cup soft tofu, mashed

¼ cup lemon juice

2 tablespoons canola oil

2 tablespoons sugar *or* honey

¾ teaspoon dry mustard

¾ teaspoon salt

½ cup onion, chopped

¼ cup sweet pickle relish (optional)

1. In blender container, combine all ingredients except pickle relish and blend until smooth.

2. Fold in pickle relish. Chill until serving time.

SWEET-AND-SOUR SAUCE

Makes 2¾ cups

1½ cups unsweetened pineapple juice

½ cup plus 2 tablespoons brown sugar *or* molasses

   or

½ cup apple juice concentrate

½ cup lemon juice

½ teaspoon garlic powder

2 tablespoons cornstarch

¼ teaspoon soy sauce

1. In small saucepan, combine all the ingredients except cornstarch. Add cornstarch to cold sauce mixture and whisk until it is totally dissolved and no lumps remain.

2. Cook over medium heat, stirring constantly, until mixture is thickened.

VINEGAR-FREE TOMATO KETCHUP

2	cups canned tomatoes, crushed, *or* 2 cups fresh tomatoes, diced
1	4-ounce can tomato paste
½	red bell pepper, chopped
¼	cup onion, chopped
⅛	cup frozen orange juice concentrate
1	bay leaf
½	teaspoon celery seed
2	carrots, cut in chunks
4-6	tablespoons lemon juice, to taste
	salt to taste (optional)
	garlic powder to taste

1. In food processor, process all ingredients except the bay leaf until smooth and well blended.
2. Transfer mixture to small saucepan, add bay leaf, and simmer uncovered over medium-low heat, stirring constantly, to desired consistency. Add more orange and/or lemon juice to taste. If you prefer a sweeter flavor, add a small amount of honey or sugar. Remove bay leaf before serving.

Makes 2 cups

RECIPE TIPS
Lemon and orange juice replace the vinegar in this ketchup.

CHEESELESS "PARMESAN" CHEESE

½	cup nutritional yeast flakes
½	cup ground sesame seeds
2	teaspoons garlic powder
1	teaspoon onion powder
1	teaspoon McKay's Chicken-Style Seasoning *or* Chicken-like Seasoning *(p. 135)*
3	teaspoons lemon juice

Combine all ingredients except lemon juice in blender or food processor. Blend until all ingredients are finely ground. Add lemon juice and process until well blended. Store in refrigerator in airtight container.

Makes 1 cup

RECIPE TIPS
This cheese browns very quickly, so add it to the top of a dish only during the last few minutes of baking. It does not melt when placed on top of a dish, but it adds the same flavor as Parmesan when mixed in with other ingredients.

CHEESELESS "CHEESE" SAUCE

1	cup roasted cashews
1	cup water
½	cup pimientos ***and/or*** roasted red peppers
¼	cup yeast flakes
¼	cup sesame seeds
¼	cup lemon juice
½-1	teaspoon salt
1	teaspoon onion powder
½	teaspoon garlic powder

Blend all the above ingredients until smooth. Use for Baked Enchilada Casserole *(p. 110)* or in the Layered Bean Dip recipe *(p. 111)*, or you can bake it in a casserole dish for 20 to 30 minutes, or until a knife inserted comes out clean. Use this baked Cheeseless "Cheese" as a dip for tortilla chips. Use it raw on top of pizza, for macaroni and cheese, lasagna, enchiladas, or other dishes that call for cheese and will be baked. The flavor is delicious.

Makes 3 cups

NEW LABELS MAKE IT EASIER TO FOLLOW DIETARY GUIDELINES

It makes good sense to read the labels on the foods you buy, and now new labels make it easier to shop smart and eat right. Many food packages already display nutrition labels that follow new regulations set by the Food and Drug Administration (FDA). These labels give information that is more complete, accurate, and easy to understand, including the following:

SERVING SIZES

For the first time, serving sizes for similar foods must be consistent, making it easier to compare nutritional values.

1. **Total calories and calories from fat.**
   The label must show both calories per serving and the number of calories from fat, information you need to budget fat intake.

2. **Daily values for nutrients.**
   Given as percentages, daily values show the food's nutritional content, based on a daily diet of 2,000 calories.

3. **Calories per gram.**
   This information indicates how many calories are in each gram of fat, carbohydrate, and protein.

RECOMMENDED DIETARY GUIDELINES

The FDA recommends the following guidelines for an optimal diet that will aid in the prevention and treatment of chronic diseases.

Total fat:

No more than 30 percent of total calories per day.

Saturated fat:

No more than 10 percent of total calories per day.

Cholesterol:

No more than 300 milligrams per day.

Sodium:

No more than 2,400 milligrams per day.

Total carbohydrates:

A minimum of 55 percent of total calories per day.

Complex carbohydrates:

A minimum of 45 percent of total calories per day.

Fiber:

A minimum of 25 grams per day.

Protein:

12 to 15 percent of total calories per day.

A PEEK INTO MY PANTRY

Let's assume you've decided to make the transition to a healthful, plant-based diet. What foods do you need to buy? Where do you buy them? Which brands are best?

It isn't as overwhelming as it sounds. Let me show you what's in my pantry, refrigerator, freezer, and vegetable bin. If you begin to stock up on these items, you'll soon have all the supplies you need for the fix-it-fast, 30-minute meals in this book.

GRAINS

Oats:

Rolled oats and quick oats are used in this book. Rolled oats have a thicker flake and take longer to cook than quick oats.

Cornmeal:

Whole-grain is best, but most grocers sell only cornmeal that has the bran and germ removed. I like to use yellow cornmeal for the nice coloring it gives to food, but white cornmeal is equally nutritious.

Couscous:

Some call this the five-minute wonder. When it comes to speed, it doesn't get any better than instant couscous. Actually a form of pasta, couscous is made from golden semolina flour, mixed with water and rolled into tiny grains. Couscous is the national dish of Morocco, Tunisia, and Algeria. Whole-wheat couscous is becoming more common; if it's not at your supermarket, check a health food store.

Flour and Corn Tortillas:

Purchase these in the refrigerator or freezer section of the supermarket. They keep well when frozen.

Popcorn:

White hull-less is my favorite type of popcorn, because it has fewer hulls and is more tender than yellow popcorn.

Rice:

Short-grain rice has a sweeter taste and tends to hold together better. Long-grain rice does not stick together and has a richer taste.

Basmati Rice:

India's favorite rice is increasingly available in the United States and Canada, even in its unrefined state. This long-grain rice has a wonderful flavor and almost floral fragrance.

Millet:

Whole millet can be found in health food stores. It has much the same flavor as rice, but is, somehow, refreshingly different.

Whole-Wheat Flour:

I'm fortunate to have a kitchen mill for grinding my own flour. For breadmaking I use "hard" white winter-wheat berries for milling. They have a higher gluten content that produces the best quality whole-wheat bread. If you are purchasing your flour already milled, for the lightest bread choose a finely milled whole-wheat flour. For pastry or other nonyeast baked products, choose an all-purpose "soft" wheat flour. Its lower gluten content produces a more tender pastry. I keep all flours in the freezer to preserve their freshness and gluten content. (Be sure to bring the flour to room temperature before using it in baking.)

Wheat Gluten:

Small amounts added to yeast-activated baked goods improve volume, texture, and shelf life.

Enriched Unbleached White Flour:

I like to keep this on hand to combine with whole-wheat flour in some recipes.

Wheat Germ:

Available raw or toasted, this product is the heart of the wheat and adds a nutty flavor to many recipes. Toasted wheat germ has a longer shelf life and a nuttier flavor, but fewer nutrients than the raw. To maintain freshness, be sure to store raw wheat germ in the freezer.

Bulgur Wheat:

Available in health food stores and some supermarkets.

Pasta:

I stock a variety of pasta shapes and sizes, such as linguine, vermicelli, angel hair, ziti, egg noodles, spirals, shells, etc. The nutritional analysis for the pasta recipes in this book is based on the standard white noodle. For a higher fiber diet, replace white noodles with whole-wheat pasta.

NUTS AND SEEDS

Get nuts and seeds at the grocery store or health food store, or for a less-expensive source, investigate your local co-op. Buy them already roasted or purchase them raw and roast them yourself in a shallow pan in a 350°F oven for 5 to 10 minutes. To preserve their freshness, store large quantities of nuts and seeds in the freezer.

Almonds:

Raw, slivered, and sliced.

Cashews:

Unsalted, roasted.

Peanut Butter:

Be a label reader. Buy peanut butter that lists only peanuts and salt on the label—no added oils, sweeteners, or preservatives.

Pecans:

Raw, chopped.

Pine Nuts:

These are great when used in pasta with pesto, or on top of salads. They are also good when toasted in a 350°F oven for 5 to 10 minutes.

Sesame Seeds:

Hulled sesame seeds are white and have a milder flavor than the unhulled brown kind. Both are fine for cooking.

Tahini:

This is a sesame seed paste, or butter, made from ground unhulled sesame seeds. It is a common ingredient in many traditional Middle Eastern dishes. You can buy it in some grocery stores and most health food stores. Tahini will separate, so be sure to mix in the oils before each use. Refrigerate after opening.

Sunflower Seeds:

Buy these raw or dry-roasted.

Walnuts

LEGUMES

Most legumes are available either dried or canned. Use either kind in the recipes in this book. Canned beans are more convenient, but they're more expensive and may contain extra salt. They can be rinsed to lower the salt content.

Cannellini or White Kidney Beans:

These beans are an Italian bean that I use in many of my favorite recipes. They are more tender than regular kidney beans, and I love their flavor.

Garbanzos (Chickpeas)

Kidney Beans

Lentils

Pinto Beans

Red Beans

Tofu:

Tofu is made from soybean curd, just as cottage cheese is made from milk. It is a high-protein staple food for vegetarians that can be used to replace dairy and egg products in recipes. I prefer the Mori-Nu tofu, which is available in soft, firm, or extra firm, determined by how much liquid is left in the soy beans. It is also available in a lite (1 percent fat) version, and the flavor is the same. Mori-Nu tofu has been sterilized so all bacteria have been destroyed. Therefore, shelf life is increased, the consumer doesn't have to soak the tofu before using it, and the tofu does not get rancid. Many people who are learning to use tofu unknowingly use rancid tofu. A foolproof way to know that your tofu is fresh is to refrigerate it after purchasing and after opening the box. Once opened, tofu can become rancid, so use within five days. Mori-Nu tofu comes in extra firm, firm, and soft consistencies. The firm Mori-Nu tofu is equivalent to the soft tofu consistency of other brands, because Mori-Nu has a higher moisture content.

FRESH FRUITS:

I purchase a variety of fresh fruits weekly — apples, oranges, seedless red grapes, bananas, and fruits in season. For a treat, our family enjoys a mango or two each week. I love lemon or lime water and also like to use these fruits as a garnish. So I purchase three or four lemons and limes each week.

DRIED FRUITS:

Watch out for fruits that are dried with sulfites. Many people are allergic to sulfites. I use a home food dehydrator, partially drying the fruits and freezing them in airtight bags. This is a real treat.

Apricots

Coconut:

I usually use the sweetened type and limit the quantity; however, the unsweetened type is better if you're trying to limit sugar. It is usually available only in health food stores.

Currants:

These are a nice change from raisins.

Dates (seedless)

Peaches

Pears

Raisins

CANNED FRUITS AND JUICES

Choose fruits that are juice-packed, have no added sugar, and contain no additives.

Cranberry Juice

Lemon Juice

Peaches

Pears

Pineapple Chunks

FROZEN FRUITS AND JUICES

Be sure to buy juices that have no added sugar. When buying frozen fruits, get those that are loose-packed and that can be quickly frozen without added sugar.

Apple Juice Concentrate:

This concentrate is naturally very sweet and can be used to flavor and sweeten many dessert recipes.

Blueberries (whole)

Cranberry Juice Concentrate

Grape Juice Concentrate

Grapefruit Juice Concentrate

Lemon Juice Concentrate

Orange Juice Concentrate

Pineapple Juice Concentrate

Raspberries (whole)

Strawberries (whole or sliced)

REFRIGERATED FRESH VEGETABLES

Most fresh vegetables, of course, should be purchased as close to serving time as possible so that you can eat them at their peak of nutritive value and flavor. Depending on seasonal availability, every week I purchase three or four types of salad greens (usually green leaf lettuce, head lettuce, Bibb lettuce, and spinach), large beefsteak tomatoes, plum tomatoes, carrots, cabbage, cucumbers, avocados, mushrooms, scallions, fresh herbs, and other salad ingredients. I use lots of broccoli, cauliflower, cabbage, zucchini, summer squash, and eggplant for a variety of vegetarian dishes. Fresh steamed vegetables are rarely turned down.

VEGETABLE BIN VEGETABLES

There are a few fresh vegetables that keep well and can be bought ahead. These will last up to a month if refrigerated.

Garlic Cloves:

I go through three or four bulbs per week. You will find that garlic is a great replacement for salt.

Green Chili Peppers

Jalapeño Peppers

Onions:

Sweet white onions are often more acceptable to those who are not exactly crazy about onions.

Potatoes:

I like russet potatoes for baking and the thin-skinned white or red potatoes for boiling or steaming. Russet potatoes work best for baked potato wedges, because the lower sugar content helps to prevent the potato from burning on the outside before the inside is cooked. I also keep a supply of white cooking potatoes on hand for use in recipes in which potatoes will be combined with other foods.

FROZEN VEGETABLES

I keep a supply of frozen vegetables in the freezer just in case I run out of a fresh vegetable.

Broccoli

Carrots (sliced and baby whole)

Cauliflower

Corn

Green Beans

Peas

Spinach (chopped)

CANNED VEGETABLES

Because of the hidden salt usually found in them, I use very few canned vegetables. Tomato paste is the exception. I use my own canned Roma tomatoes for making delicious Italian sauce.

Green Chilies (chopped)

Olives (black)

Pimientos (chopped)

Roasted Red Peppers:

If you are too busy to roast your own, these canned whole roasted red peppers are great to fall back on.

Tomato Paste (low-salt)

Tomatoes (canned diced or chopped, low-salt)

Tomatoes (canned whole with low salt)

TEXTURED VEGETABLE PROTEIN PRODUCTS

Worthington Foods, Loma Linda Foods, Morningstar Farms, and Natural Touch are all name brands of canned and frozen meat substitutes. These products, called "textured vegetable proteins," are made from gluten (protein from wheat flour) and soy products. They are free of animal fat, cholesterol, and preservatives. They are typically lower in fat (especially saturated fat) and calories than their meat and egg counterparts. These foods add a meatlike flavor and texture to recipes. They are nationally available in natural food stores and grocery stores.

DAIRY PRODUCTS AND SUBSTITUTES

Read labels carefully. Buy low-fat milk, cheeses, and sour creams. Skim milk and part-skim cheeses have the lowest fat content. Remember that even 2 percent milk is really 32 percent fat, and that 1 percent milk is really 16 percent fat. Only skim milk is fat-free. The nutrition analysis in this book is based on using skim milk and part-skim cheeses in the low-fat dairy options.

Powdered Tofu Milk:

I like this as a replacement for dairy milk. And it has a smoother texture and better flavor than soy milk. The brands I like are Tofu White, by Magic Mill, and

Better Than Milk. Both are available at health food stores. Use this milk to replace dairy milk in recipes, over cereal, and for drinking.

Cheese:

You'll find recipes for nondairy cheese, Parmesan cheese, and whipped cream in the Variations section of this book. Tofu cheese, almond cheese, etc., are available in health food stores, and make good cheese replacements.

Eggs:

Lacto-ovovegetarians and others who need to lower fat and cholesterol in their diet discard the yolks to eliminate cholesterol. One-third cup of tofu blended with a small amount of water until whipped-egg consistency can replace one egg, or 3 tablespoons water mixed with 1 tablespoon cornstarch can replace one egg.

Evaporated Skim Milk:

Although it comes in a can, don't confuse this with canned sweetened condensed milk, a totally different and much less healthy product. Canned evaporated skim milk is a good replacement for cream or half-and-half in recipes. You can even use it to make an acceptable substitute for whipped cream by refrigerating it until it is very cold. Then, adding a little sweetener and vanilla, whip it at high speed with an electric mixer for about six minutes. You'll never miss the extra fat.

Mozzarella Cheese, part-skim:

This is a low-fat cheese that is made without rennin (rennin is from the lining of a calf's stomach and is used in most cheeses). More cheeses are now being made without rennin. Mozzarella cheese can be grated and frozen for future use.

Parmesan Cheese:

Although this cheese is high in fat, a tiny bit adds a lot of flavor and can be substituted for a much larger portion of other cheeses in recipes. In the Variations section of this book there is a substitute for Parmesan cheese.

SEASONINGS AND HERBS

Fresh or Dried Herbs:

Fresh herbs have so much more flavor in recipes than dried herbs, but I keep the dried herbs on hand for times that I cannot get fresh ones. If you can grow your own fresh herbs, that is the best. Just chop the leaves of the fresh herbs and use in recipes at the proportions of three times the amount of dried herbs. For example, 1 teaspoon of dried basil can be replaced with 3 teaspoons of fresh basil. To preserve more of the flavor, store fresh herbs in the refrigerator in a vase of water, and store dried herbs in the freezer or refrigerator. The following herbs and seasonings are the ones I use the most and always try to have on hand in the fresh and dried form.

Basil

Celery Leaves (crushed)

Celery Seed (ground)

Chili Powder

Cinnamon (ground and stick)

Coconut Extract

Coriander

Cumin

Dillweed

George Washington Broth Mix:

This powdered broth mix comes in beefy brown, golden, and onion flavors and is available at health food stores and some grocery stores. It has a vegetable oil base and contains no animal fat.

Fresh Ginger Root or Ginger

Granulated Garlic or Garlic Powder

Lemon Peel (grated)

McKay's Chicken-Style Seasoning:

An excellent chicken-flavored seasoning for broth and soups, this seasoning has a vegetable oil base and contains no animal fat. It is available at health food stores. You can make your own chicken seasoning mix by using the Chicken-like Seasoning recipe in the Variations section of this book.

Mint

Mizo (soybean paste):

Mizo is available at Oriental or health food stores.

Mustard (dried)

Nutritional Yeast Flakes:

This is edible brewer's yeast (*Saccharomyces cerevisiae*) in flake form. Don't confuse it with the brown powdered brewer's yeast product, which is very bitter. These yeast flakes are yellow and have a cheese-like flavor. I use them for seasoning popcorn and wherever a cheese flavor is wanted.

Onion Powder

Oregano Leaves (chopped):

There are two types of oregano—Italian and Mexican. They are very different in taste. Use Italian with Italian foods and

Mexican with Mexican foods.

Paprika:

I prefer Hungarian paprika because of its nice red color.

Parsley (chopped)

Poppy Seeds

Rosemary

Sage

Savory

Soy Sauce (low-salt)

Thyme

Turmeric:

Used to season and add yellow color to foods.

Vanilla Extract (white and regular):

Use white vanilla when flavoring white or light-colored foods, such as ice cream or whipped toppings. It is available in grocery stores in the cake-decorating section. The flavor is the same as regular vanilla. Be sure to use pure vanilla, not imitation.

MISCELLANEOUS

Active Dry Yeast:

Dry yeast comes in two types—regular and rapid-rise. If you use instant yeast, you allow the bread dough to rise only once in bread tins. Be sure to read the label carefully to determine which yeast you are buying. For the best results, use the yeast by the date listed on the package. Store in the refrigerator or freezer to maintain freshness.

Brown Sugar

Cornstarch:

This is used for thickening sauces, soups, and gravies.

Carob Chips:

Carob is the ground dried fruit of the carob tree, which grows principally in the Mediterranean region. Because products made from carob resemble chocolate, some people consider the fruit a chocolate substitute. Carob does not taste as rich as chocolate, but it has its own unique, pleasant flavor. Not only is it low in fat, low in calories, and contains no caffeine, but it is naturally sweet and contains fiber, calcium, phosphorus, and potassium. Carob is available in several forms: as powder, sweetened or unsweetened carob chips, blocks for baking or cooking, and powdered mixes for hot carob beverages. Carob chips are available at some grocery stores and at all health food stores. I use the sweetened carob chips for most of my recipes.

Club Soda:

This low-calorie carbonated beverage makes a sparkling addition to punches.

Honey

Molasses:

Store molasses at room temperature before opening, then keep it in the refrigerator, where it will keep for up to three months. Molasses is available in both light, dark, or blackstrap. I prefer the milder flavor of light molasses.

Nonstick Vegetable Cooking Spray:

I use a nonstick spray (such as Pam) for oiling baking pans or preparing a skillet for sautéing. It is a good way to save on fat without sacrificing flavor.

Tapioca:

Instant brands are the most convenient.

Vegetable Oils:

Keep all oils in the refrigerator. Oil kept on the pantry shelf can turn rancid and lose its fresh flavor.

Canola Oil:

Canola oil is made from rapeseed. Like olive oil, it is high in monounsaturated fat, which studies show is the preferred type of fat to lower cholesterol. It is a mild-tasting vegetable oil that does not break down at high temperatures and can be used in all types of cooking. It is quickly gaining popularity at the supermarket.

Olive Oil (cold-pressed):

High in monounsaturated fat, this oil is a good choice for fighting cholesterol. There are several varieties from light all the way to extra-virgin, which is almost green, the color of the olives, and has the strongest taste. I prefer the taste of light olive oil for most cooking. The extra-virgin is perfect for a hearty tomato sauce.

FOR YOUR INFORMATION

MEASUREMENT EQUIVALENTS

3 teaspoons	=	1 tablespoon (15 ml.)
16 tablespoons	=	1 cup (about 250 ml.)
4 tablespoons	=	$1/4$ cup (about 60 ml.)
1 ounce	=	30 milliliters
$1/3$ cup	=	$5 1/3$ tablespoons (about 80 ml.)
2 cups	=	1 pint (about 500 ml.)
4 cups (2 pints)	=	1 quart
4 quarts (liquid)	=	1 gallon

SUBSTITUTIONS:

Many of the recipes you are currently using can be adapted to lower their fat content and improve their nutritional value. Experiment to find the alternatives you like best.

Whole Eggs

For recipes that do not need leavening, replace one whole egg with:

- two egg whites.
- Morningstar Farms Better 'n Eggs or $1/4$-$1/3$ cup blended tofu *(both are cholesterol-free alternatives)*.
- 1 tablespoon cornstarch dissolved in 3 tablespoons of water.

Sugar

Replace $1\frac{1}{4}$ cups sugar plus $\frac{1}{4}$ cup liquid with 1 cup honey.

Whole Milk

Replace 1 cup fresh whole milk with 1 cup nondairy milk alternative, such as tofu milk, almond milk, or cashew-rice milk.

Sour Cream

Replace sour cream with Tofu Sour Cream (a cholesterol-free, low-fat alternative; recipe in Variations section).

Whipped Cream

Replace whipped cream with Tofu Whipped Cream (a cholesterol-free, low-fat alternative; recipe in the Variations section).

Mayonnaise

Replace mayonnaise with the Soy Ranch Mayonnaise (a cholesterol-free, low-fat nondairy alternative; recipe in the Variations section).

HOW THE RECIPES ARE ANALYZED:

Calories per serving and a nutrient breakdown are included for every recipe. The dairy and nondairy options for each recipe are calculated separately. The nutrients listed include grams of carbohydrate, protein, fat, and fiber. The fat is broken down into polyunsaturated, monounsaturated, saturated, and total fat. The nutrients listed in milligrams include cholesterol, sodium, potassium, iron, and calcium.

The recipes were developed for people who love good food, but who are interested in lowering their intake of calories, sugar, fat, cholesterol, and sodium to maintain healthful eating patterns. The levels of these restricted nutrients in some recipes may be higher than those prescribed by a physician for specific health problems. The calorie and nutrient breakdown of each recipe is derived from computer analysis, based primarily on

information from the U.S. Department of Agriculture. The values are as accurate as possible and reflect the following assumptions:

- All nutrient breakdowns are listed per serving.
- When a range is given for the number of servings (example: serves 6-8), the analysis is calculated on the larger number of servings.
- When a range is given for an ingredient (example: 3 to $3\frac{1}{2}$ cups flour) the analysis is calculated on the lesser amount.
- When ingredients are stated as "optional" or "to taste," they have been deleted from the nutrient information.
- When a recipe gives the option of using oil or water, the analysis is based on using water.
- When the recipe gives the option of baking in a pan coated with nonstick vegetable spray, the analysis will be based on the baking option.
- When the recipe calls for honey or sugar, the analysis will be based on honey.
- When the recipe calls for a choice of honey, sugar, or fruit juice, the analysis will be based on fruit juice.
- If a recipe calls for honey or sugar, the recipe will be analyzed with honey.

						FATS										DIABETIC EXCHANGE					
RECIPE	Serving	Calories	Protein gm	Carbs gm	Chol mg	Total Fat	Poly gm	Mono gm	Sat gm	Fiber gm	Folate ug	Vit C mg	Sodium mg	Iron mg	Calcium mg	Bread Ex	Protein Ex	Veg Ex	Milk Ex	Fruit Ex	Fat Ex
BREAKFAST																					
Almond-Oat Scones (dairy)	1 scone	174	4	25	0.2	6	2	3.5	0.5	0.3	5	9	157	1	29	1	0	0	0	0	1
Almond-Oat Scones (nondairy)	1 scone	170	4	25	0	5.5	1.5	3	0	0.3	5	9	156	1	9.3	1	0	0	0	0	2
Apple Pancakes (dairy)	2 cakes	116	4	22	0.5	1	0.4	0.6	0	2	8	2	229	1	66	1	0	0	0	0.5	0.2
Apple Pancakes (nondairy)	2 cakes	119	3	23	0	1.8	0.6	0.6	0	2	6.3	2	208	1	27	1	0	0	0	0.3	0.4
Belgian Waffles (dairy)	1 waffle	193	7	41	0.5	0.7	0.2	0.1	0	3.5	14	7	360	2	91	1	0.3	0	0.1	1	0
Belgian Waffles (nondairy)	1 waffle	196	7	42	0	0.5	0.5	0	0	3.5	13	8	356	1.8	56	1.2	0.3	0	0.2	1	0
Apricot Sauce	1/4 cup	72	1	19	0	0	0	0	0	2	3	7	6	0.5	18	0	0	0	0	1	0
Breakfast Burritos (dairy)	1 burrito	288	16	50	0	3	2	1	0	3	23	25	500	3	131	3	0.5	1	0	0	0.5
Breakfast Burritos (nondairy)	1 burrito	258	15	46	0	3	1	2	0	4	15	14	320	4	84	4	1.5	0	0	0	0.5
Cheryl's Almond Granola	1/4 cup	150	5	26	0	3	1	2	0	3	8	14	58	1.5	21	1	0	0	0	0.5	0.5
Choles.-free Pancakes (dairy)	2 cakes	178	7	31	0.5	3	1	1.5	0.5	2	13	1	310	2	100	1.5	0	0	0	0	1
Choles.-free Pancakes (nondairy)	2 cakes	180	7	31	0	3	1	1.5	0.5	2	11	0.5	304	2	54	1.5	0	0	0	0	1
Currant-Sesame Scones (dairy)	1 scone	170	4	24	0	6.5	2	3	0.5	2	3	9	156	1.5	45	1	0	0	0	0	1
Currant-Sesame Scones (nondairy)	1 scone	170	4	20	0	6	2	3	0.5	2	2	9	150	1.5	33	1	0	0	0	0	1
Five-Grain Cooked Cereal	1/2 cup	180	6	36	0	1.5	0.5	0.5	0	5	19	0.5	180	2	19	2	0	0	0	0	0
Low-Fat Granola	1/2 cup	320	8	62	0	5	3	1	0.5	5	28	39	15	3	50	2	0	0	0	2	1
Peach-Berry-Banana Fruit Shake (dairy)	1 cup	213	8	46	2	0	0	0	0	3	98	81	89	0.5	250	0	0	0	1	2	0
Peach-Berry-Banana Fruit Shake (nondairy)	1 cup	198	6.8	42	0	11	0.5	0	0	4	85	83	100	1.5	59	0	1	0	0	2	0
Peach or Apricot Butter	2 tbsp	10	0	2	0	0	0	0	0	2	0	4	1	0	2	0	0	0	0	0.1	0
Pineapple-Banana Breakfast Shake (dairy)	1 cup	190	8	39	1	1	0	0	0	4	34	35	62	1.5	180	0	0	0	0.5	2	0
Pineapple-Banana Breakfast Shake (nondairy)	1 cup	180	7	38	0	1	0	0	0	4	25	35	150	2	55	0	0.5	0	0	2	0
Quick-cooking Seven-Grain Cereal	1 1/4 cups	187	8	35	0	2	1	1	0	4	13	0.5	150	2	62	2	0	0	0	0.5	0.5
Red Berry Spread	2 tsp	6	0	1	0	0	0	0	0	0	2	5	0	0	2	0	0	0	0	0	0
LUNCH: SANDWICHES																					
Garbanzo Bean Sandwiches	1 pita	158	7	30	0	2	1	0.5	0	5	19	10	205	3	44	1	0	0.5	0	0	0.5
Grilled Vegetable Sandwich With Creamy Herb Dressing	1 sandwich	340	13	34	0	5	1	3	0.5	10	99	300	34	45	62	3	0	3	0	0	1
Guilt-free Burgers	3" burger	153	6	28	0	2.5	1	0.5	0	3	9	2	70	1	16	2	0	0	0	0	0.5

Nutritional Analysis

RECIPE	Serving	Calories	Protein gm	Carb gm	Chol mg	Total Fat	Poly gm	Mono gm	Sat gm	Fiber gm	Folate ug	Vit C mg	Sodium mg	Iron mg	Calcium mg	Bread Ex	Protein Ex	Veg Ex	Milk Ex	Fruit Ex	Fat Ex
Ital.-Style Vegetarian Hoagie	4" sandwich	138	5	21	0	4	0.5	2	0.5	3	11	27	228	2	72	1	0	1	0	0	1
Lentil Patties in Pita Pocket	1 pita half	180	11	35	0	1	0.5	0	0	1	80	5	246	2	35	2	0.5	0.5	0	0	0
Mexican Chili Burgers	1 burger	96	4	19	0	0.7	0	0	0	2	9	4	64	1	32	1	0	0.5	0	0	0
Oven-baked Mexi-Fries	1/2 cup	145	3	30	0	2	1	0.5	0	4	23	6	54	2	106	2	0	0.5	0	0	0
Oven-baked Seasoned Fries	1/2 cup	238	5	51	0	2	0.5	1	0	5	22	26	80	3	21	3	0	0	0	0	0.5
Roasted Vegetable Pitas With Creamy Herb Dressing	1 pita half	225	9	45	0	4	0.5	1	0.5	5	83	600	231	88	80	1	0	5	0	0	0.5
Toasted Bagels With Roasted Red Pepper Spread	1 bagel half	149	7	30	0	1	0	0	0	2	28	225	224	34	53	1	0	3.5	0	0	0

LUNCH: SENSATIONAL MAIN DISH SALADS

RECIPE	Serving	Calories	Protein gm	Carb gm	Chol mg	Total Fat	Poly gm	Mono gm	Sat gm	Fiber gm	Folate ug	Vit C mg	Sodium mg	Iron mg	Calcium mg	Bread Ex	Protein Ex	Veg Ex	Milk Ex	Fruit Ex	Fat Ex
Haystacks	1 cup	180	4	34	0	2	0	0	0	2	20	3	262	0	15	1	0	0	0	0	0.5
Summer Harvest Chicken-Potato Salad	1/2 cup	260	10	48	0	4	2	1	0.5	4	38	117	251	15	100	3	0.5	1	0	0	0.5
Soy Ranch Dressing	1 tbsp	25	0	1.5	0	2	0.5	1	0	0	0.5	1	18	0	2	0	0	0	0	0	0.5
Waldorf Potato Salad	1/2 cup	187	3	35	0	5	1.5	3	0	4	13	19	45	0.5	17	1.5	0	0	0.5	0.5	1
Caesar Salad	1 cup	82	6	12	0	1.5	0.5	0	0	3	113	25	218	3	100	1	0	1	0	0	0
Garden Greek Salad	1 cup	133	6	23	0	3	1	2	0	5	80	43	30	2	48	1	0	1	0	0	0.5

LUNCH: SOUPS

RECIPE	Serving	Calories	Protein gm	Carb gm	Chol mg	Total Fat	Poly gm	Mono gm	Sat gm	Fiber gm	Folate ug	Vit C mg	Sodium mg	Iron mg	Calcium mg	Bread Ex	Protein Ex	Veg Ex	Milk Ex	Fruit Ex	Fat Ex
Chilled Chunky Gazpacho	1 cup	94	4	18	0	2	0.5	1	0	4	43	81	205	2	80	0	0	3	0	0	0
Chilled Minted Pea Soup	1 1/2 cups	155	11	26	0	0.5	0.5	0	0	10	136	16	176	2.4	54	1.5	1	0.5	0	0	1
Creamy Broccoli-Rice Soup	1 1/2 cups	140	7	27	0	1	0	0	0	4	95	75	88	1	130	1	0	1	0	0	0
Creamy Garlic Potato Soup	1 cup	175	4	33	0	2.4	0	1.5	0	3	13	16	70	0.5	70	1.5	0	0.5	0.5	0	0.5
Italian Vegetable Soup	1 cup	99	5	20	0	0.5	0	0	0	4	23	12	140	2	44	1	0	1	0	0	0
Vegetable Chili	1 cup	250	12	40	0	2	1	0	0	12	115	28	280	46	88	2	0	0	0	0	0
Vegetable Split-Pea Soup	1 1/2 cups	180	12	33	0	0.5	0	0	0	13	141	3	41	2	41	2	1	0.5	0	0	0

MAIN DISH DINNERS: PASTA

RECIPE	Serving	Calories	Protein gm	Carb gm	Chol mg	Total Fat	Poly gm	Mono gm	Sat gm	Fiber gm	Folate ug	Vit C mg	Sodium mg	Iron mg	Calcium mg	Bread Ex	Protein Ex	Veg Ex	Milk Ex	Fruit Ex	Fat Ex
Angel Hair Vegetable Toss	1 1/2 cups	260	13	49	64	2	0	0	0.5	9	113	69	280	4	100	2	0.5	3	0	0	0.5
Asparagus "Alfredo" Pasta Bows	1 cup	290	13	52	0	4	0.5	0	0	3	93	21	214	3	56	2	1	1	0	0	1
Chili Macaroni	1 cup	192	11	38	0	1.5	0.5	0	0	6.5	52	70	230	4	84	1.5	1	1.5	0	0	0
Fresh Basil Pesto With Pasta	1 cup	303	11	45	0	9	3.5	4	1.5	2	1	4.8	220	3.5	21	3	1	0.5	0	0	2
Linguine With Fresh Tomato Sauce	1 cup	303	12	65	0	2	0	0	0	8	85	9	298	138	122	4	1.5	5	0	0	0

Nutritional Analysis

RECIPE	Serving	Calories	Protein gm	Carbs gm	Chol mg	Total Fat	Poly gm	Mono gm	Sat gm	Fiber gm	Folate ug	Vit C mg	Sodium mg	Iron mg	Calcium mg	Bread Ex	Protein Ex	Veg Ex	Milk Ex	Fruit Ex	Fat Ex
Pasta Tossed With Seasoned Olive Oil and Fresh Basil	1 cup	259	9	52	0	1	0.5	0	0	3	24	16	262	3.6	91	3.5	1	2	0	0	0
Pasta With Basil and Tomatoes	1 cup	226	8	40	0	2.5	1.5	1.4	2.5	3	9	10	350	3	60	3	1	1	0	0	0.5
Sun-dried Tomato-Red Pepper Pesto With Pasta	1 cup	420	23	80	0	6	1	1	0.5	12	213	120	222	62	168	2	1	5	0	0	1
Vegetable Lasagna	2½" sq.	253	8	50	0	2	0	1	0	5	43	265	334	37	98	2	0	4	0	0	0
Vermicelli With Chunky Vegetable Sauce	1 cup	326	13	70	0	2	0.5	0	0	8	73	600	521	88	113	2	0	6	0	0	0
Fettucine Primavera Alfredo	1 cup	280	11	55	0	2	0.5	0.5	0	4	55	50	168	13	76	3	0	2	0	0	0

MAIN DISH DINNERS: RICE AND COUSCOUS

RECIPE	Serving	Calories	Protein gm	Carbs gm	Chol mg	Total Fat	Poly gm	Mono gm	Sat gm	Fiber gm	Folate ug	Vit C mg	Sodium mg	Iron mg	Calcium mg	Bread Ex	Protein Ex	Veg Ex	Milk Ex	Fruit Ex	Fat Ex
Basil-roasted Vegetables Over Couscous	2 cups	255	8	52	0	4	0	2.5	0.5	8	28	78	149	1	34	2	0	2	0	0	1
Basmati Rice Seasoned With Dried Fruits and Nuts	1 cup	281	5	51	0	7	1.5	4	0.5	3	7	2	260	1	18	2.5	0	0	0	1	2.5
Brown Rice With Vegetables and Tomato Pesto	1 cup	150	4	31	0	2	0.5	1	0	4	35	33	81	1	46	1.5	0	1.5	0	0	0
Couscous Alfresco	1 cup	303	9	59	0	3.5	1	1.5	0.5	8	110	18	105	1	30	3.5	0	1.5	0	0	1
Curried "Chicken" and Broccoli Couscous	1 cup	290	12	48	0	6	2	2	0.5	8	70	120	200	70	50	1.5	0.5	3	0	0	0.5
Garden Vegetable Couscous	1 cup	208	8	36	0	4	1.5	2	0.5	6	39	12	260	2	61	2	0	1	0	0	0.5
Grilled Vegetables Over Rice	1 cup	230	8	43	0	3	1	1	0.5	8	154	24	19	3	56	2.5	0	1	0	0	0.5
Hearty Rice Skillet	1 cup	225	10	41	0	3.5	1	2	0.5	8	104	15	154	3	50	2.5	0.5	1	0	0	0.5
Herbed "Chicken" Couscous and Vegetables	1 cup	238	13	32	0	6.5	3.5	2	1	4	38	12	310	2	33	2	1	0.5	0	0	1
Pesto Rice and Beans	1 cup	400	16	40	0	12	6	4	2	3	230	6	81	5	130	3.5	2	0.5	0	0	2.5
Pesto Risotto	1 cup	136	5	20	0	5	2	2	1	2	55	15	25	1	25	1	0	0	0	0	3
Roasted-Pepper Bruschetta	1 piece	107	4	18	0	2.5	0.5	1	0.5	3	10	66	176	1	33	1	0	0.5	0	0	0.5
Spring Vegetable Curry	1 cup	435	14	65	0	12	1	3	6	12	130	34	128	4	86	3.5	0.5	1.5	0	0	2.5
Stir-fried Asian Vegetables	1 cup	315	8	61	0	6	2	2	0.5	2	35	20	266	3	36	3.5	0	1	0	0	1
Teriyaki Stir-Fry Over Rice	1½ cups	385	11	81	0	6	235	6	1.5	7	75	398	400	60	84	2.5	0.5	4	0	0	2
Vegetable Medley Quiche in Rice Crust	1 piece	219	10	35	0	5	1.5	2	1	4	47	68	230	2	75	3	1	1	0	0	2

MAIN DISH DINNERS: POTATOES

RECIPE	Serving	Calories	Protein gm	Carbs gm	Chol mg	Total Fat	Poly gm	Mono gm	Sat gm	Fiber gm	Folate ug	Vit C mg	Sodium mg	Iron mg	Calcium mg	Bread Ex	Protein Ex	Veg Ex	Milk Ex	Fruit Ex	Fat Ex
Cheesy Potato Skins (dairy)	½ cup	145	5	18	8	4	0.5	2	1	2	10	11	104	0.5	100	1	0.5	0	0	0	0.5
Garden-fresh Potato Toss	1 cup	250	6	57	0	1	0	0.5	0	6	40	55	20	3	41	3	0	1	0	0	0

152

RECIPE	Serving	Calories	Protein gm	Carbs gm	Chol mg	Total Fat	Poly gm	Mono gm	Sat gm	Fiber gm	Folate ug	Vit C mg	Sodium mg	Iron mg	Calcium mg	Bread Ex	Protein Ex	Veg Ex	Milk Ex	Fruit Ex	Fat Ex
Garlic Potatoes With "Chicken"	1 cup	226	8	37	0	5.5	2	2.5	0.5	5	19	23	200	1	33	2	0.5	0.5	0	0	1
Mexican Baked Potatoes With Bean-and-Corn Salsa	1 potato	385	23	70	8	3.5	0.5	0.5	1.5	12	127	322	350	46	300	4	2	3	0	0	0
Roots at 500°F	1 cup	195	3	42	0	3	0.5	2	0.5	2	32	20	41	1	26	2	0	0.5	0	0	1.5
Vegetable Potato Salad	1 cup	145	6	30	0	1	0	0	0	5	153	46	235	1	61	1.5	0	1.5	0	0	0
MAIN DISH DINNERS: MEXICAN																					
Baked Enchilada Casserole	3" square	290	16	40	15	6	0.5	1	3	6	72	7	345	3	310	2.5	1.5	0.5	0	0	0
Bean Enchiladas	1 enchilada	290	16	42	0	6	2	3	1	3	58	37	390	4	220	2.5	1	1.5	0	0	2
Layered Bean Dip	1/2 cup	196	9	30	0	5	1	2.5	1	8	135	135	400	22	113	2	0.5	0	0	0	1
No-Guilt Refried Beans	1/2 cup	100	6	20	0	0.5	0	0	0	5	75	3	310	2	49	1	0.5	0	0	0	0
Oven-baked Vegetable Fajitas	1 fajita	375	15	71	0	6	1.5	2	1	13	33	80	306	3	135	4	0	1.5	0	0	0.5
Tamale Pie	1 cup	420	8	84	0	7	1.5	2.5	2	6	51	13	296	3	68	4	0	2	0	0.5	1
Vegetable Burritos Grande	1 burrito	294	14	47	8	7	1	3	2	7	114	28	310	3	175	3	1	1	0	0	1
White Bean Quesadillas	1 quesadilla	294	20	52	20	4	3	1	1	5	114	550	299	88	117	2	1	5	0	0	1.5
MAIN DISH DINNERS: LEGUMES																					
Indian Lentils and Rice	1 1/2 cups	374	20	58	0	8	2	3	1.5	3	260	22	343	7	93	3.5	1.5	0.5	0	0	1
Mazidra	1/2 cup	122	7	16	0	3.5	0.5	2.5	0.5	1	112	5	277	2	25	1	0.5	0.5	0	0	0.5
MAIN DISH DINNERS: PIZZA																					
French Bread Pizza With Beans and Chunky Vegetables	5" piece	324	14	58	0	5	2	2	1	7	131	198	310	33	140	3.5	0.5	1	0	0	2
Fresh Tomato-Herb Pizza	1 piece	425	21	70	0	12	6	5	1	15	309	707	312	120	283	3	2	1.5	0	0	2
Grilled Vegetable Pizza With Spinach-Walnut Pesto	1 piece	145	4	24	0	3.5	0.5	2	0.5	2	70	9	42	2	37	1.5	0	0.5	0	0	0.5
Pesto Pizza	1 piece	175	5	26	0	6	1	3	0.5	2	29	20	104	2	43	1.5	0	1	0	0	1
Roasted Vegetable Pizza	1 piece	350	16	55	0	13	5	5	2	11	267	606	344	100	180	3	1.5	0.5	0	0	3
Spinach-Pesto Salad Pizza	1 piece	316	12	21	0	10	5	5	1	3	82	48	74	4	79	1	1	1	0	0	2
DESSERTS																					
Blueberry Crisp	1 piece	330	4	57	0	9	3	5	1	3	15	13	18	2	30	1	0	0	0	2	2
Fresh Apple-Pineapple Cream Pie (dairy)	1 piece	247	6	36	1	9	3	5	0.5	3	15	8	111	1	129	1	0	0	0.5	1	1

FATS | **DIABETIC EXCHANGE**

Nutritional Analysis

RECIPE	Serving	Calories	Protein gm	Carbs gm	Chol mg	Total Fat	Poly gm	Mono gm	Sat gm	Fiber gm	Folate ug	Vit C mg	Sodium mg	Iron mg	Calcium mg	Bread Ex	Protein Ex	Veg Ex	Milk Ex	Fruit Ex	Fat Ex
DESSERTS																					
Fresh Apple-Pineapple Cream Pie (nondairy)	1 piece	227	5	38	0	7	3	4	1	2	8	9	215	1.5	30	1.5	0.5	0	0	1	1.5
Glazed Fresh Peach Pie	1 piece	250	3	40	0	8	2	4	0.5	3	9	8	68	1	11	1	0	0	0	1	2
Glazed Fresh Strawberry Pie	1 piece	224	3	33	0	9	3	5	0.5	3	25	64	70	1	20	1	0	0	0	0.5	1.5
Low-Fat Raspberry Cheesecake	1 piece	160	2	30	0	4	1.5	2	0	1	8	3	50	0	56	0.5	0	0	0	0	1
Peanut Butter Cookies	1 cookie	63	1	8	0	3	1	1.5	0.5	1	4	0	82	0	5	0.5	0	0	0	0	0.5
Pumpkin Pie	1 piece	294	3.5	47	0	9	2.5	5	1.5	2	13	2	210	2	33	3	0	0	0	0	1.5
Strawberry-Almond Torte	1 piece	340	9	52	0	9	4	4	1	2	20	47	217	2	55	1	1	0	0	0.5	1.5
VARIATIONS AND SUBSTITUTIONS																					
Basil-Pine Nut Pesto	1 tbsp	33	1	0.5	0	3	1	1	0.5	0	0.5	0	0	0	3	0	0	0	0	0	0.5
Cheeseless "Cheese" Sauce	1 tbsp	30	1	3	0	2	0.5	1	0	0.5	19	49	26	7	12	0	0	0	0	0	0
Cheeseless "Parmesan" Cheese	1 tbsp	27	2	3	0	1	0.5	0.5	0	1.5	158	0	15	1	31	0	0	0	0	0	0
Chicken-like Seasoning	1/4 tsp	0	0	0	0	0	0	0	0	0	0	0	0	0	0	0	0	0	0	0	0
Classic Fresh Salsa	1/4 cup	40	2	9	0	0	0	0	0	2	8	31	201	1	70	0	0	1.5	0	0	0
Creamy Cucumber Dressing	1 tbsp	4	0	0	0	0	0	0	0	0	1	1	23	0	4	0	0	0	0	0	0
Creamy Herb Dressing	1 tbsp	5	0	1	0	0.5	0	0	0	0	0	1	35	0	5	0	0	0	0	0	0
Low-Fat Creamy Onion-Dill Dressing	1 tbsp	11	0.5	2	0	0	0	0	0	0	2	1	100	0	15	0	0	0	0	0	0
Nondairy Creamy Onion-Dill Dressing	1 tbsp	6	0	1	0	0	0	0	0	0	0	0	35	0	4	0	0	0	0	0	0
Ranch Soy Mayonnaise	1 tsp	8	0	0	0	0.5	0	0	0	0	0	0	3	0	0	0	0	0	0	0	0
Spinach-Walnut Pesto (dairy)	1 tbsp	12	0.5	0.5	0	1	0.5	0.5	0	0	15	2	4	0	4	0	0	0	0	0	0
Spinach-Walnut Pesto (nondairy)	1 tbsp	12	0	0	0	1	0.5	0.5	0	0	14	2	9	0	5	0	0	0	0	0	0
Sweet-and-Sour Sauce	2 tbsp	25	0	6	0	0	0	0	0	0	5	13	6	0	5	0	0	0	0	0.5	0
Tartar Sauce	1 tbsp	6	0	1	0	0	0	0	0	0	0	1	53	0	2	0	0	0	0	0	0
Thick and Chunky Salsa	1/4 cup	64	3	15	0	0	0	0	0	3	21	33	201	1	49	0	0	2	0	0	0
Tofu Whipped Cream	1 tbsp	11	1	2	0	0	0	0	0	0	0	0	80	0	4	0	0	0	0	0	0
Tofu Yogurt or Sour Cream	1 tbsp	13	1	2	0	0	0	0	0	0	0	0	130	0	11	0	0	0	0	0	0
Vinegar-free Tomato Ketchup	1 tbsp	14	0.5	3	0	0	0	0	0	0.5	4	7	72	0	9	0	0	0.5	0	0	0

FATS — *DIABETIC EXCHANGE*

FIND YOUR BODY MASS INDEX [BMI]

Table 1

HEIGHT

WEIGHT

WEIGHT	| 5 FT						HEIGHT IN INCHES									6 FT					
	56	57	58	59	60	61	62	63	64	65	66	67	68	69	70	71	72	73	74	75	76
100	22	22	21	20	20	19	18	18	17	17	16	16	15	15	14	14	14	13	13	13	12
105	24	23	22	21	21	20	19	19	18	18	17	16	16	16	15	15	14	14	14	13	13
110	25	24	23	22	22	21	20	20	19	18	18	17	17	16	16	15	15	15	14	14	13
115	26	25	24	23	23	22	21	20	20	19	19	18	18	17	17	16	16	15	15	14	14
120	27	26	25	24	23	23	22	21	21	20	19	19	18	18	17	17	16	16	15	15	15
125	28	27	26	25	24	24	23	22	22	21	20	20	19	18	18	17	17	17	16	16	15
130	29	28	27	26	25	25	24	23	22	22	21	20	20	19	19	18	18	17	17	16	16
135	30	29	28	27	26	26	25	24	23	23	22	21	21	20	19	19	18	18	17	17	16
140	31	30	29	28	27	27	26	25	24	23	23	22	21	21	20	20	19	19	18	18	17
145	33	31	30	29	28	27	27	26	25	24	23	23	22	21	21	20	20	19	19	18	18
150	34	33	31	30	29	28	27	27	26	25	24	24	23	22	22	21	20	20	19	19	18
155	35	34	32	31	30	29	28	28	27	26	25	24	24	23	22	22	21	20	20	19	19
160	36	35	34	32	31	30	29	28	28	27	26	25	24	24	23	22	22	21	21	20	20
165	37	36	35	33	32	31	30	29	28	28	27	26	25	24	24	23	22	22	21	21	20
170	38	37	36	34	33	32	31	30	29	28	27	27	26	25	24	24	23	22	22	21	21
175	39	38	37	35	34	33	32	31	30	29	28	27	27	26	25	24	24	23	23	22	21
180	40	39	38	36	35	34	33	32	31	30	29	28	27	26	25	25	24	24	23	23	22
185	42	40	39	37	36	35	34	33	32	31	30	29	28	27	27	26	25	24	24	23	23
190	43	41	40	38	37	36	35	34	33	32	31	30	29	28	27	27	26	25	24	24	23
195	44	42	41	39	38	37	36	35	34	33	32	31	30	29	28	27	27	26	25	24	24
200	45	43	42	40	39	38	37	36	34	33	32	31	30	30	29	28	27	26	26	25	24
205	46	44	43	41	40	39	38	36	35	34	33	32	31	30	29	29	28	27	26	26	25
210	47	46	44	43	41	40	38	37	36	35	34	33	32	31	30	29	29	28	27	26	26
215	48	47	45	44	42	41	39	38	37	36	35	34	33	32	31	30	29	28	28	27	26
220	49	48	46	45	43	42	40	39	38	37	36	35	34	33	32	31	30	29	28	28	27
225	51	49	47	46	44	43	41	40	39	38	36	35	34	33	32	31	31	30	29	28	27
230	52	50	48	47	45	44	42	41	40	38	37	36	35	34	33	32	31	30	30	29	28
235	53	51	49	48	46	44	43	42	40	39	38	37	36	35	34	33	32	31	30	29	29
240	54	52	50	49	47	45	44	43	41	40	39	38	37	36	35	34	33	32	31	30	29
245	55	53	51	50	48	46	45	43	42	41	40	38	37	36	35	34	33	32	32	31	30
250	56	54	52	51	49	47	46	44	43	42	40	39	38	37	36	35	34	33	32	31	30
255	57	55	53	52	50	48	47	45	44	43	41	40	39	38	37	36	35	34	33	32	31
260	58	56	54	53	51	49	48	46	45	43	42	41	40	38	37	36	35	34	33	33	32
265	60	57	56	54	52	50	49	47	46	44	43	42	40	39	38	37	36	35	34	33	32
270	61	59	57	55	53	51	49	48	46	45	44	42	41	40	39	38	37	36	35	34	33
275	62	60	58	56	54	52	50	49	47	46	44	43	42	41	40	38	37	36	35	34	34
280	63	61	59	57	55	53	51	50	48	47	45	44	43	41	40	39	38	37	36	35	34

DETERMINING YOUR BMI

BMI = weight (kg)/height (meters)²

This chart determines your BMI so that you can use the chart on page 7. Find your height in inches across the top of Table 1 (above) and then locate your weight down the left-side column. Where the weight and height boxes come together, that is your BMI.

Healthy Weigh Plan

155

Index of Recipes

Nutrition & Lifestyle

MEDICAL CONSULTING

Cheryl D. Thomas-Peters, RD
James A. Peters, MD, DrPH, RD

1201 Dual Highway #123
Hagerstown, MD 21740

(909) 795-7300

www.CherylRD.com

- RECENT NUTRITION UPDATES

- RECENT HEALTH AND LIFESTYLE INFORMATION

- NEW RECEIPES AND COOKING TIPS

- WEIGHT LOSS UPDATES AND TIPS

- ARRANGE FOR NUTRITION AND LIFESTYLE SEMINARS AT YOUR LOCATION

- NUTRITION AND LIFESTYLE PHYSICIAN/DIETITIAN CONSULTS AVAILABLE

MORE *FAMILY* READING

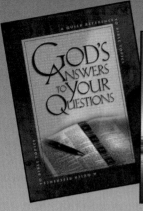

God's Answers to Your Questions
You ask the questions; it points you to Bible texts with the answers

He Taught Love
The true meaning hidden within the parables of Jesus

Jesus, Friend of Children
Favorite chapters from *The Bible Story*

Bible Heroes
A selection of the most exciting adventures from *The Bible Story*

The Storybook
Excerpts from Uncle Arthur's *Bedtime Stories*

My Friend Jesus
Stories for preschoolers from the life of Christ, with activity pages

Quick and Easy Cooking
Plans for complete, healthful meals

Fabulous Food for Family and Friends
Complete menus perfect for entertaining

Choices: Quick and Healthy Cooking
Healthy meal plans you can make in a hurry

More Choices for a Healthy, Low-Fat You
All-natural meals you can make in 30 minutes

Tasty Vegan Delights
Exceptional recipes without animal fats or dairy products

Fun With Kids in the Kitchen Cookbook
Let your kids help with these healthy recipes

Health Power
Choices you can make that will revolutionize your health

Secret Keys
Character-building stories for children

Winning
Gives teens good reasons to be drug-free

FOR MORE INFORMATION:
- mail the attached card
- or write
  Home Health Education Service
  P.O. Box 1119
  Hagerstown, MD 21741
- or visit www.thebiblestory.com

FOR SCHOOL-AGE CHILDREN
The Bible Story
This is the most accurate and complete set of children's Bible story books available. More than 400 Bible stories are included, with full color paintings at every page-opening. Unlike television, these stories introduce children to heroes you would be proud to have them imitate. These stories are also an excellent tool for loving parents who want their children to grow up making right decisions and making them with confidence. Ten volumes, hardcover.

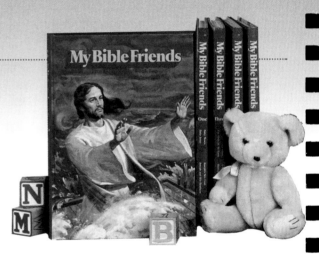

The Desire of Ages
This is E. G. White's monumental best-seller on the life of Christ. It is perhaps the most spiritually perceptive of the Saviour's biographies since the Gospel According to John. Here Jesus becomes more than a historic figure—He is the great divine-human personality set forth in a hostile world to make peace between God and man. Two volumes, hardcover.

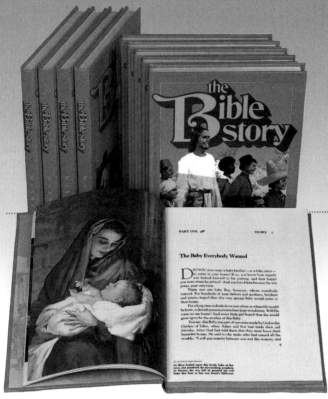

FOR PRESCHOOL CHILDREN
My Bible Friends
Imagine your child's delight as you read the charming story of Small Donkey, who carried tired Mary up the hill toward Bethlehem. Or of Zacchaeus the Cheater, who climbed a sycamore tree so he could see Jesus passing by. Each book has four attention-holding stories written in simple, crystal-clear language. And the colorful illustrations surpass in quality what you may have seen in any other children's Bible story book. Five volumes, hardcover. Also available in videos and audio cassettes.

Uncle Arthur's Bedtime Stories
For years this collection of stories has been the center of cozy reading experiences between parents and children. Arthur Maxwell tells the real-life adventures of young children—adventures that teach the importance of character traits like kindness and honesty. Discover how a hollow pie taught Robert not to be greedy and how an apple pie shared by Annie saved her life. Five volumes, hardcover.

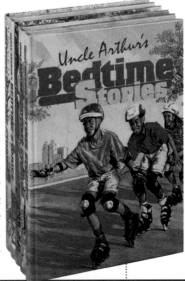